MACHINE L

AND

DATA SCIENCE

An Introduction to Statistical

Learning Methods with R

first edition

Daniel D. Gutierrez

Published by:

2 Lindsley Road
Basking Ridge, NJ 07920 USA

https://www.TechnicsPub.com

Cover design by Mark Brye
Edited by Carol Lehn and Erin Elizabeth Long

ISBN, print ed.9781634620963
ISBN, Kindle ed.9781634620970
ISBN, ePub ed.9781634620987
ISBN, PDF ed.9781634620994

First Printing 2015

Library of Congress Control Number: 2015948863

Table of Contents

Introduction

When I was growing up, I was enamored with the *"Foundation* trilogy" by renowned science fiction writer and professor Isaac Asimov. A prominent character in the story line was Hari Seldon, a mathematics professor who developed a scientific field called "psychohistory" that combined history, sociology, and mathematical statistics, allowing him to predict the future in probabilistic terms. As a result, I was hooked on the concept of prediction at a very young age, so becoming a data scientist was a profession that felt quite natural for me. And machine learning is a tool that I liken to Seldon's Prime Radiant, a device that stores "psychohistorical equations" showing the future development of humanity.

I've been a data scientist (or some semblance of it) for many years, long before the "data science" moniker came on the scene. It's taken decades of professional evolution for the title "data scientist" to come into existence, and I couldn't be more delighted. Much has been debated recently in industry online forums about whether "data science" is a term that adequately describes the field. I feel it does a magnificent job since much of what a data scientist does is experimental in nature–the scientific method definitely is in force with what I do on a day-in, day-out basis. I personally feel it is more descriptive and more accurate than "data mining" or "business intelligence," two other terms that went through rigorous hype-cycles in years gone by. I'm quite satisfied with "data scientist" because I do feel that I'm a scientist experimenting with data.

Here is how I see the scientific method applied to problems solved with data science:

- **Formulate a question:** The question can pertain to the explanation of a specific observation like "does the number of deals the sales team can close always increase with the number of calls made to the prospect?" This stage involves finding data sets that provide evidence for answering the question. When applying the scientific method to data science, determining a good question can be very difficult and affects the final outcome of the investigation.

- **Come up with a hypothesis**: A hypothesis is a conjecture that may explain the observed behavior. The hypothesis is based on knowledge obtained while formulating the question. A typical hypothesis might be something like "the likelihood of approval for a mortgage loan is dependent on the prospective homeowner's income and credit score."

- **Prediction**: This step involves determining the logical consequences of the hypothesis, and with data science that means selecting an appropriate machine learning algorithm for solving the problem. Ideally, the prediction must also distinguish the hypothesis from likely alternatives; if two hypotheses make the same prediction, observing the prediction to be correct is not evidence for either one over the other. This is why some areas of machine learning require experimenting with different algorithms using the same data sets to see how they perform. This step also requires you to "train" the algorithm with a restricted set of data.

- **Testing**: This is an investigation of whether the real world behaves as predicted by the hypothesis. As a data scientist, you'll use another data set that's been held out from the training process to estimate its predictive capabilities. The purpose of this *experiment* is to determine whether observations of the real world agree with or conflict with the predictions derived from a hypothesis. If they agree, confidence in the hypothesis increases; otherwise, it decreases. Agreement does not assure that the hypothesis is true, and future experimentation may reveal problems.

- **Analysis**: This involves determining what the results of the experiment show and deciding on the next actions to take. Through data visualization, you might discover that the data you're using for machine learning is inadequate for the predictive power you require, so you take a step back and re-visit the question formulation stage. You may wish to repeat the experiment with different data sets to see if you get the same results. Once a hypothesis is strongly supported by the data, a new question can be asked to provide further insight on the same topic.

In this sense, the scientific method is an iterative process that continues until you develop a strong "theory" you can apply moving forward.

Machine learning is the primary toolset used by data scientists for making predictions and testing the validity of hypotheses. Let's continue with providing a brief understanding for what machine learning is and what data scientists use it for. The term "machine learning" represents a confluence of disciplines: computer science, mathematical statistics, probability theory, and data visualization. We'll see in later chapters that there are two primary forms of machine learning: supervised learning, which is the predictive form, and unsupervised learning, which is the discovery form. If you truly wanted to understand the depths of various machine learning algorithms, you'd have to understand the principles of several areas of mathematics such as mathematical statistics, probability theory, calculus, linear algebra, partial differential equations, and combinatorics. Fortunately, we're using R in this book, so we won't need to dig into the foundations of the algorithms. We'll just learn how to use them.

How This Book is Organized

This book is organized in the manner you might approach an actual data science project involving machine learning. This is not to say what I have provided here is the only way to do machine learning, but I think it is representative for how data scientists go about their work. This recipe has served me well over the years, and I hope to impart my experience now to you in this book. Here is a breakdown of the book by chapter:

- **Chapter 1: Machine Learning Overview**. This chapter contains an overview of data science and why businesses are showing an increasing level of interest in this technology. We'll also give a brief overview of machine learning and how it plays an integral role in data science today. Then we'll review the different types of machine learning, provide examples of each, and draw a general outline of the machine learning process. We'll discuss how the R environment plays an integral role in experimental machine learning through use of its multitude of packages.

- **Chapter 2: Data Access**. The first step in machine learning is to access an appropriate data set for the purpose of getting the data content inside of the R environment so we can begin performing analysis. In this chapter, we'll use R to access data in a number of ways from different data sources (comma separate value, Excel, JSON, Twitter, and Google Analytics). We'll also pave the way for accessing data in SQL databases. Once the data are in R, we'll see how to set up an appropriate development environment for data analysis and machine learning.

- **Chapter 3: Data Munging**. An often tedious but very important early step when starting a machine learning project is "data munging," also known as "data wrangling" or "data transformation". In other words, examining and refining the data set for further analysis. In this chapter we'll look at creating a data munging toolbox consisting of a variety of techniques: revise variable names, create new variables, discretize numeric values, date handling, binary categorical variables, merge/order/reshape data sets, data manipulation using `dplyr`, handle missing data, and feature scaling. Other topics include feature engineering, data sampling, and the data pipeline. Finally, we'll see how Principal Component Analysis can achieve useful dimensionality reduction.

- **Chapter 4: Exploratory Data Analysis**. Once the data is in the proper form, the next thing to do is to become intimately acquainted with the data in terms of how they can be used for machine learning. In this chapter we'll use exploratory and expository visualizations to understand data properties, find patterns in data, and suggest modeling strategies. We'll start by using R's statistical features: numeric summaries, levels of factor variables, means/medians/modes, quantiles, standard deviation, and variation. We'll also use R's graphing features: histograms, boxplots, bar plots, density plots, scatter plots, QQ plots, and heat maps.

- **Chapter 5: Regression**. In this chapter, we introduce the most common form of machine learning: supervised learning. We'll closely examine the workhorse of predictive analytics: linear regression. We'll see how to set up a linear model in R and calculate a regression line to be used for prediction. Both single and multiple covariate regression will be demonstrated including regression with factor variables.

- **Chapter 6: Classification**. In this chapter, we introduce another common form of supervised machine learning: classification. We'll use a number of useful R packages to explore a variety of classification algorithms including logistic regression, classification trees, naïve Bayes, K nearest neighbor, support vector machines and neural networks. We'll also consider ensemble methods such as the popular random forest algorithm. Lastly, we'll take a look at gradient boosting machines, which have been quite popular in machine learning competitions.

- **Chapter 7: Evaluating Model Performance**. This chapter discusses how we choose one model over another and evaluate predictive performance. We'll talk about areas of statistical learning that affect performance such as overfitting, bias vs. variance tradeoff, confounders, and data leakage. We'll also define metrics for measuring regression and classification model accuracy. Lastly, we'll demonstrate the cross validation process designed to minimize a model's generalization error.

- **Chapter 8: Unsupervised Learning**. This chapter introduces unsupervised machine learning using two clustering techniques: hierarchical clustering and K-means clustering. With hierarchical clustering, we use an agglomerative approach to produce a dendigram or tree structure showing how close things are to each other. Then with K-means clustering, we use an iterative partitioning approach to obtain a final estimate of cluster centroids and assign each data point to clusters. Lastly, we'll quickly review another popular unsupervised technique called principal component analysis.

I've chosen several fundamental parameters for this introductory text on machine learning. These parameters are the result of my desire to make the process as simple and straightforward as possible:

- We won't use sophisticated (some might say obfuscated) R programming techniques in the code examples. Sure, you might be able to represent a programming problem in a single statement with nested function calls, but understanding it would be contrary to the learning process. So instead we'll keep things simple, especially if this is your first introduction to R.

- As much as I'd like to, we will not use the popular `ggplot2` graphics package in this book. Instead, we'll opt to use the base R graphics functions. The base R functions are arguably more straightforward.

- We'll try to keep the number of R packages and data sets to a minimum, focusing on the most common packages aligned with the topics of each chapter, plus some support packages that make our lives easier.

INTENDED AUDIENCE FOR THIS BOOK

This book is intended for a fairly general audience. If you are an analyst in either the private or public sector and you need to expand your analytics skills past the feature-set you find in a tool like Excel, then this book is for you. If you are a software developer and you have a new requirement to implement machine learning in your code, then this book is for you. If you're a researcher in an academic discipline and you need to get up to speed with data science and machine learning methodologies, then this book is for you. The common thread in these audience segments is the sincere desire to learn the basics and quickly get productive in this field. I hope to reach readers from across a wide spectrum of disciplines, so my use of examples in various problem domains will be very general.

I necessarily will assume you know some R programming or can pick it up in parallel with the material in this book. This book does not teach R but rather uses R as a tool for getting up to speed with machine learning. The good thing is that only very basic R is used in this book. The not so good thing is that R is notoriously hard to learn for someone new to the language. The R code scripts used in the book are straightforward for the most part, and where necessary I will add comments in the text to describe what's going on. I won't confuse the effort of introducing the concepts of machine learning with tricky code.

I hope you're motivated to take on the task of getting up to speed with machine learning. This book will provide you with the framework for doing so, but there are many additional resources to help you with the process which I'll outline below.

WHAT YOU WILL NEED

This book stands on its own with respect to any additional hardware or software requirements, with one very obvious exception: you will need to use the R statistical programming environment, which is fortunately open source and therefore free to use. You can obtain the R software by visiting: www.r-project.org. It installs and runs on a wide variety of UNIX platforms, Windows, and MacOS. While you're at the R Project site, feel free to take inventory of all learning materials including the R Manuals, the R Journal, Books, and other R Documentation.

One other piece of software that is highly recommended to be used with this book is the RStudio Integrated Development Environment (IDE). To download RStudio, visit: www.rstudio.com. RStudio is a powerful and productive user interface for R. It's free and open source, and it works great on Windows, Mac, and Linux. I used RStudio extensively in writing this book, and I will assume you're doing so as well. Although you can get by with the rudimentary programming environment provided with the R distribution, RStudio includes many features attractive to programmers such as:

- Syntax highlighting, code completion, and smart indentation
- Workspace browser and data viewer
- Plot history, zooming, and flexible image and PDF export
- Integrated R help and documentation
- Searchable command history
- Execute R code directly from the source editor
- Easy management of multiple working directories using projects

You'll also need a number of additional R packages (extensions to the R statistical environment) throughout the book. These packages also are open source and can be downloaded and installed from within R. When needed for a particular example, I will advise you how to install and use the package.

I've also made a conscious effort to avoid requiring the reader to seek out, download, and install data sets for use in the examples in the book. Instead, in most cases I've made every attempt to only use data sets that come native with the base R distribution. In some cases, we may use data sets that come along with specific R packages. In a few other cases I have used data sets beyond R, but I will advise you how to access the data sets.

R Code and Figures

You'll find that this book contains many examples of R programming code and results from specific commands returned by the R environment. In order to represent code in the book, I've prefixed all commands entered in the R console with the familiar ">" symbol. We'll also use a special "code font" so you can distinguish code from book text. In addition, responses from R will be shown using the same code font, but without the ">" symbol. As you're reading the book, I encourage you to enter in all code samples into R for yourself in order to get a feeling for using the environment. It is also a good idea to experiment with each code sample by changing different elements in order to see the resulting effect.

In order to make your learning experience as palatable as possible, I've made all the R source code used in this book available with my book's description on the publisher's website: https://technicspub.com/analytics/. Included are all of the graphs and plots (many in color) that appear as grayscale figures in the book. This should make the understanding of some graphs and plots easier. You can check this repository in the future for any updates to the code.

Going Beyond This Book

Once you've completed the material in this book, you'll need some direction about where to go next with learning machine learning. Fortunately, machine learning has evolved enough in the past few years that there is growing interest in the subject, and as a result there are many resources to help you expand your knowledge. There is no shortage of educational materials; you just need to consider how far you wish to go. To get you started, here is a short list of resources:

- **Free online courses**: In the age of the MOOC (massive open online course), you can find a number of excellent free courses on machine learning and related subjects. Two of my favorite MOOC platforms are Coursera (www.coursera.org) and edX (www.edx.org). I'm partial to the Coursera offerings since I beta tested much of the machine learning educational content and served many times as a Community Teaching Assistant (TA).
- **Blogs**: There are many excellent blogs out there that provide useful articles that you can use to learn more about the field. Fortunately, there is a particularly good site that aggregates the content of many popular R blogs all under one roof: www.r-bloggers.com. By frequenting this site or by subscribing to its daily e-mail list, you can keep abreast of this quickly evolving field.
- **Meetup groups**: It is a good idea to join one or more Meetup groups in your area that focus on data science related topics depending on your specific interest. In my home town of Los Angeles, we have excellent groups for both Machine Learning and R.
- **Twitter feeds**: I have personally learned a great deal from the people I follow on Twitter. One person can't reasonably monitor an entire industry, so my Twitter friends provide a valuable service by alerting me to new trends, articles, methods, products, services, conferences etc. To get started, search on the most relevant hashtags: #MachineLearning, #DataScience, #R, and #BigData to find some of your own favorites.

CONTACTING THE AUTHOR

You can contact me in a number of ways. Feel free to visit my consulting firm's website: www.amuletanalytics.com or find me on LinkedIn. But probably the best place to catch up with me would be on Twitter (@AMULETAnalytics) where you can follow my musings on data science, machine learning, and big data.

Chapter 1
Machine Learning Overview

Machine learning can be thought of as a set of tools and methods that attempt to infer patterns and extract insight from observations made of the physical world. For example, if you wanted to predict the price of a house based on the number of rooms, number of bathrooms, square footage, and lot size, you can use a simple machine learning algorithm (e.g. linear regression) to learn from an existing real estate sales data set where the price of each house is known, and then based on what you've learned, you can predict the price of other houses where the price is unknown. In practice, this sort of prediction requires data, and in contemporary applications, this often means a high volume of data (frequently in the terabyte range and beyond). The quantity of data is important to the predictive power of machine learning; as the old adage in data science goes, "more data always trumps a clever algorithm."

The subject of machine learning is one that has matured considerably over the past several years. Machine learning has grown to be the facilitator of the field of *Data Science*, which is, in turn, the facilitator of *Big Data*. Machine learning, however, is not a totally new discipline; its general principles have been around for quite some time, just under different names: "data mining," "knowledge discovery in databases," and "business intelligence." These terms have been used to describe what is now called *machine learning*. Prior to that, "statistics" and "data analysis" were terms used to describe the process of gleaning knowledge from data. I believe machine learning is the best term used to describe my field to date, and the hashtag #MachineLearning has certainly heated up the Twitter-verse with an impressive number of references. Machine learning is also considered to be a branch of *artificial intelligence* that concerns the construction and study of systems that can learn from data. Much of machine learning's current embodiment depends on new capabilities of hardware utilizing cloud storage solutions and high-performing parallel architectures such as Apache Hadoop and Spark.

Officially, the first use of the term "machine learning" was in 1959 by Arthur Samuel, at the time working at IBM, who described it as the field of study that gives computers the ability to learn without being explicitly programmed. Fast forward to 1998, when Tom Mitchell, Chair of the Machine Learning Department at Carnegie Mellon University, described a learning program this way:

> *A computer program is said to learn from experience E with respect to some class of tasks T and performance measure P, if its performance at tasks in T, as measured by P, improves with experience E.*

Mitchell's widely quoted formal definition is broad enough to include most tasks that we would conventionally call "learning" tasks. As an example of a machine learning problem under this definition, consider task T: classifying spam e-mails, performance measure P: percent of e-mail properly classified as spam, and training experience E: data set of e-mails with given classifications (i.e., spam or ham). The spam classifier is one of the first modern applications of machine learning to solve a real-life business problem, and it is incorporated into most of today's e-mail applications.

Another very important axiom to remember when starting up a new machine learning project is offered by American mathematician John Tukey, who is often revered in statistics circles for his many contributions to statistical methods as well as his seminal 1977 book "*Exploratory Data Analysis*":

> *The combination of some data and an aching desire for an answer does not ensure that a reasonable answer can be extracted from a given body of data.*

This maxim implies that a machine learning practitioner needs to know when to give up, when the data you have are just not sufficient to answer the question you're trying to answer. The familiar "garbage in, garbage out" axiom still applies to machine learning.

TYPES OF MACHINE LEARNING

This book will introduce you to the essential tenets of machine learning. As the main enabler of data science and big data, machine learning has garnered much interest from a broad range of industries as a way to increase the value of enterprise data assets. In this book, we'll examine the principles underlying the two primary types of machine learning algorithms: *supervised* and *unsupervised,* based on the R statistical environment.

Supervised machine learning is typically associated with prediction, where for each observation of the predictor measurements (also known as feature variables), there is an associated response variable value. Supervised learning is where a model that relates the response to the predictors is trained with the aim of accurately predicting the response for future observations. Many classical learning algorithms, such a linear regression and logistic regression, operate in the supervised domain.

Unsupervised machine learning is a more open-ended style of statistical learning. Instead of using labeled data sets, unsupervised learning is a set of statistical tools intended for applications where there is only a set of feature variables measured across a number of observations. In this case, prediction is not the goal because the data set is unlabeled, i.e., there is no associated response variable that can supervise the analysis. Rather, the goal is to discover interesting things about the measurements on the feature variables. For example, you might find an informative way to visualize the data or discover subgroups among the variables or the observations.

One commonly used unsupervised learning technique is k-means clustering, which allows for the discovery of "clusters" of data points. Another technique, called principal component analysis (PCA), is used for dimensionality reduction, i.e., reduction of the number of feature variables while maintaining the variation in the data in order to simplify the data used in other learning algorithms, speed up processing, and reduce the required memory footprint.

Use Case Examples of Machine Learning

In this section, I present a few examples of real-life business problems with machine learning solutions. In order to provide such examples, it is useful for you to see the original requirements of the project, review the data sets and each feature variable, and understand how a solution can be judged in terms of a specific metric for success. You might even decide to attempt a solution of your own after you complete reading this book. To do all these things, I'll highlight a few Kaggle (www.kaggle.com) data challenges that have attracted thousands of data scientists from around the world to compete for monetary awards.

Competitors in these data science challenges were to consider the following characteristics when working to find a winning solution:

- What problem does it solve and for whom?

- How is the problem being solved today (if at all)?

- What are the data sets available for the problem and where do they come from?

- How are the results of the problem solution to be exposed (e.g., BI dashboard, algorithm integrated into an online application, a static management report, etc.)?

- What type of problem is this: revenue leakage ("saves us money") or revenue growth ("makes us money")?

Algorithm evaluation methods were diverse for the various competitions. The most commonly used method was to minimize the value of a calculated *root mean square error* (RMSE), which was evaluated on predictions made for a supplied test set. The RMSE evaluation method will be explained in Chapter 7. Another evaluation method was an area under the *ROC curve* also known as AUC.

Some sponsors of Kaggle competitions participate in order to acquire new directions for their products or services, while others try to recruit the winners as employees. For you, as a rising data scientist, the challenges serve as valuable training grounds in which to hone your machine learning skills.

ACQUIRE VALUED SHOPPERS CHALLENGE

Consumer brands often offer discounts to attract new shoppers to buy their products. The most valuable customers are those who return after this initial incented purchase. With enough purchase history, it is possible to predict which shoppers, when presented with an offer, will buy a new item. However, identifying the shopper who will become a loyal buyer prior to the initial purchase is a more challenging task.

The Acquire Valued Shoppers Challenge asked participants to predict which shoppers are most likely to repeat purchase. To aid with algorithmic development, data scientists were provided complete, basket-level, pre-offer shopping history for a large set of shoppers who were targeted for an acquisition campaign. The incentive offered to each shopper and their post-incentive behavior was also provided. The monetary prize for this competition was $30,000.

The project provided nearly 350 million rows of completely anonymized transactional data from over 300,000 shoppers. Once unzipped, the data size amounts to 22GB, more than what can fit into the memory of most laptops. With a data volume in this range, the project can be considered "Big Data," so a well-known vendor made a special offer to participants. Revolution Analytics (Microsoft) offered the use of their Revolution R Enterprise in the Amazon Web Services (AWS) cloud for free. By spinning up a Linux box in AWS, memory capacity can reach 64GB RAM, so the competitor could try out the Parallel External Memory Algorithms included in Revolution R Enterprise. This contest is representative of the challenge of coping with the exponential growth in real-world data projects.

The plot in Figure 1-1 shows the number of repeated trips to the store plotted against the offer value in dollars on the x-axis. The data are shaded by market, a geographical area.

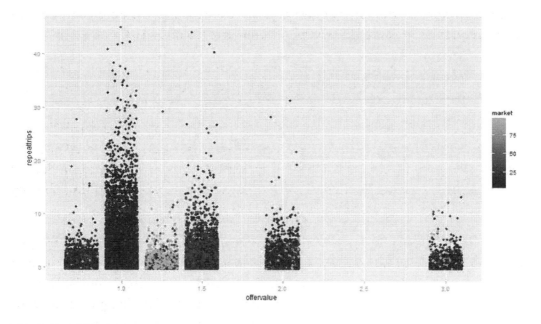

Figure 1-1 Exploratory plot using the Acquire Valued Shoppers data
(http://blog.revolutionanalytics.com/2014/04/predict-which-shoppers-will-become-repeat-buyers.html)

NETFLIX

Probably the first notable data science competition was sponsored by Netflix. The celebrated Netflix Prize sought to substantially improve the accuracy of predictions about how much someone is going to enjoy a movie based on their movie preferences. On September 21, 2009, Netflix awarded the $1 million grand prize to team "BellKor's Pragmatic Chaos." Team BellKor edged out team "The Ensemble," with the winning submission coming just 24 minutes before the conclusion of the nearly three-year-long contest.

Machine learning algorithms used to solve the Netflix Prize were evaluated using the RMSE metric. RMSE, besides being a well-known metric and a single number, has the useful property that it amplifies the contributions of egregious errors, both false positives and false negatives. These are important properties to understand about any recommendation system. Of course, it is true that simple prediction accuracy does not address many of the other important aspects of making (and taking) a recommendation. It doesn't deal with, for example, guessing in what order recommendations should be made. Nevertheless, the teams used extraordinary measures to lower their

RMSE in order to win the competition. In the end, the winning solution was able to improve the Netflix recommendation algorithm by 10%.

The Bellkor solution to the Netflix Prize problem involved many advanced techniques in machine learning: collaborative filtering, matrix factorization with temporal dynamics, Restricted Boltzmann Machines (RBM), a new blending algorithm based on Gradient Boosted Decision Trees (GBDT), and some very protracted methods for feature engineering. These methods are beyond the introductory nature of this book, but you can learn a lot by reviewing the winning entries. You can download papers describing the top four finishers for the Netflix Prize by visiting: www.netflixprize.com.

Interestingly, the winning Netflix Prize solution was never actually deployed because the algorithm failed to scale well in a production environment; it was unable to yield results on the huge Netflix data sets on a timely basis. But the null result of the Netflix Prize competition did provide insight into what constitutes a viable machine learning solution—although accuracy obviously is important, it also must scale in production. Ultimately, the company found that the additional accuracy gains measured did not seem to justify the engineering effort needed to bring them into a production environment.

ALGORITHMIC TRADING CHALLENGE

The Algorithmic Trading Challenge was a forecasting competition with the goal of developing new models to predict the stock market's short-term response following large trades. Contestants were asked to derive empirical models to predict the behavior of bid and ask prices following such "liquidity shocks." Modeling market resiliency worked to improve trading strategy evaluation methods by increasing the realism of "back-testing" simulations, which currently assume zero market resiliency. Solutions to the challenge required a firm understanding of various market dynamics that needed to be part of the model.

The 58-day challenge, completed in January 2012, attracted 111 teams competing for $10,000 in prize money. The challenge was sponsored by Capital Markets Cooperative Research Center, an Australia-based group of researchers, universities, and industry partners.

Competitors used a variety of machine learning algorithms in search of the optimal solution: linear regression, K-nearest neighbors, support vector machines, random Forest, k-means, and ensemble methods. Algorithm performance evaluation for the competition was via RMSE for each prediction, calculated separately for the bid and ask at each time step following a liquidity shock. The winning model was the one with the lowest cumulative RMSE across the entire prediction set. The winner of the challenge was Ildefons Magrans, a postdoc machine learning researcher from Spain with a Ph.D. in electrical engineering, who managed to minimize the RMSE performance metric using the random forest algorithm in R.

HERITAGE HEALTH PRIZE

This machine learning problem is probably the granddaddy of all Kaggle challenges because of the number of data science teams that participated and the size of the monetary reward offered for winning solutions. Sponsored by the Heritage Provider Network (HPN), the goal of the project was to come up with an algorithm that would help reduce the cost of healthcare—definitely a noble pursuit.

More than 71 million individuals in the United States are admitted to hospitals each year according to the latest survey from the American Hospital Association. Studies have concluded that in 2006, well over $30 billion was spent on unnecessary hospital admissions. Is there a better way? Is it possible to identify those most at risk earlier and then ensure they get the treatment they need? HPN believes it is possible and sponsored the Kaggle challenge to develop a machine learning algorithm that uses available patient data to predict and prevent unnecessary hospitalizations.

The competitors were asked to create an algorithm that predicts how many days a patient will spend in a hospital during a calendar year. Once known, health care providers can develop new care plans and strategies to reach patients before emergencies occur, thereby reducing the number of unnecessary hospitalizations. This will result in increasing the health of patients while decreasing the cost of care. In short, a winning solution will change health care delivery as we know it, from an emphasis on caring for the individual after they get sick to a true health care system.

The competition ran for two years, from April, 2011 to April, 2013. The competition's first place finisher, a team named POWERDOT, was awarded a cash prize of $500,000. You can visit the HPN website for the competition: www.heritagehealthprize.com. Here you can download the patient information data sets and a number of papers that describe the solutions of the milestone winners. The most successful solutions involved ensembles of random forests coupled with a creative selection of feature variables.

Beyond the above use case examples from past Kaggle competitions, here is a short list of additional problem domains for solution by machine learning (although there are many more):

MARKETING

- Predict Lifetime Value (LTV): Predict the characteristics of high LTV customers; this supports customer segmentation, identifies up-sell opportunities, and supports other marketing initiatives.
- Churn: Determine the characteristics of customers who churn (i.e., customer defection); this enables a company to develop adjustments to an online algorithm that allows them to reach out to churners.
- Customer segmentation: Allows you to understand qualitatively different customer groups to answer questions like what makes people buy, stop buying, etc.
- Product mix: What mix of products offers the lowest churn rate? For example, giving a combined insurance policy discount for home and auto yields a low churn rate.
- Cross-selling/up-selling and recommendation algorithms: Given a customer's past browsing history, purchase history, and other behavioral characteristics, what are they likely to want to purchase (or upgrade to) in the future?
- Discount targeting: What is the probability of encouraging the desired behavior with a discount offer?
- Reactivation likelihood: What is the likelihood of reactivation for a given customer?
- Google Adwords optimization and ad buying: Determine the optimal price for different search keywords and ad slots.

SALES

- Lead prioritization: Determine the likelihood that a given sales lead will close.
- Sales forecasting: Provide strategic planning and insight into the sales forecasting process.

SUPPLY CHAIN

- Demand forecasting: Determine optimal inventory levels for different distribution centers, enabling a lean inventory and preventing out of stock situations.

RISK MANAGEMENT

- Fraud detection: Predict whether or not a transaction should be blocked because it involves some kind of fraud, e.g., credit card fraud or Medicare fraud.
- Accounts payable recovery: Predict the probably that a liability can be recovered, given the characteristics of the borrower and the loan.

CUSTOMER SUPPORT

- Call center management: Call center volume forecasting (i.e., predicting call volume for staffing purposes).
- Call routing: Determine wait times based on caller ID history, time of day, call volumes, products owned, churn risk, LTV, etc.

HUMAN RESOURCES

- Talent management: Establish objective measures of employee success.
- Employee churn: Predict which employees are most likely to leave.
- Resume screening: Score resumes based on the outcomes of past job interviews and hires.
- Training recommendation: Recommend a specific training program based on employee performance review data.

GOOGLE FLU TRENDS

So far, we've seen a number of successful uses of machine learning as well as many potential uses. Let's take a brief look at a failure of machine learning and examine why it did not succeed. In February, 2013, Google Flu Trends (GFT) made headlines—but not for a reason that Google executives or the creators of the flu tracking system would have hoped. *Nature* reported that GFT was predicting more than double the proportion of doctor visits for influenza-like illness than the Centers for Disease Control and Prevention (CDC), which bases its estimates on surveillance reports from laboratories across the United States. This happened despite the fact that GFT was built to predict CDC reports. Given that GFT is often held up as an exemplary use of big data, what lessons can we draw from this error?

GFT tried to use the search keywords people would use in Google, like "I have a cough," to predict the rate of flu in a particular geographical location at a particular time. Early on in the study, the prediction accuracy was good, and there was much optimism because using Google technology was much more cost-effective than the CDC method. The problem, which wasn't immediately realized, was that the search keywords used by people would change over time, and in addition, there were changes to Google's search algorithm. These differences affected the algorithm's performance and resulted in poor predictive accuracy over time.

PROCESS OF MACHINE LEARNING

It is useful to survey the entire process of machine learning in order to determine a roadmap to follow when working on a data science project. In this section, I will provide a detailed work flow that you can use when doing machine learning that is general enough to encompass pretty much any project. If you discover specific additions or variations you'd like to make to the process based on the requirements for a particular domain space, feel free to create your own diagram that you can reuse in the future. The diagram in Figure 1-2 depicts this process in general terms.

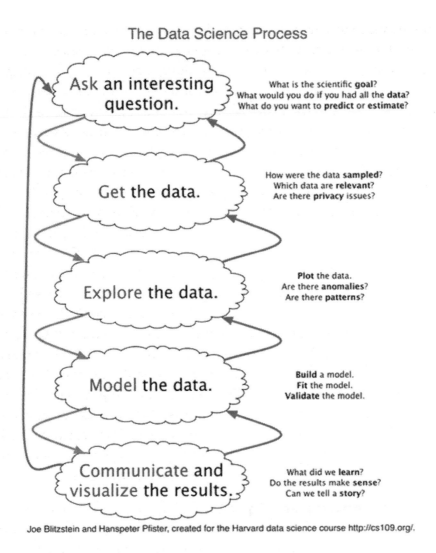

The Data Science Process

Ask an interesting question.

What is the scientific **goal**?
What would you do if you had all the **data**?
What do you want to **predict** or **estimate**?

Get the data.

How were the data **sampled**?
Which data are **relevant**?
Are there **privacy** issues?

Explore the data.

Plot the data.
Are there **anomalies**?
Are there **patterns**?

Model the data.

Build a model.
Fit the model.
Validate the model.

Communicate and visualize the results.

What did we **learn**?
Do the results make **sense**?
Can we tell a **story**?

Joe Blitzstein and Hanspeter Pfister, created for the Harvard data science course http://cs109.org/.

Figure 1-2 The data science process upon which machine projects are based

Let's go over the data science process step by step, as it will serve as a template for the rest of the book. As you gain more experience, you'll want to enhance this basic model with more nuanced approaches, but even with adjustments, the process will be largely the same.

1. **Understand the problem**: It is important to fully understand the problem domain, enlisting the help of domain experts to explain business considerations, provide data sets, define key variables, and most importantly, state the goals of the project, i.e., what is to be

predicted or discovered. A recipe for disaster with any machine learning project is to start without clear goals. If the benefactor of the project simply says to you, "Here's some data, now go do your magic," you might as well run for the hills. It will be very difficult to provide results with such unrealistic expectations. Instead, take your time during this integral step of the process and make sure that everyone who is invested in the success of the project weighs in on the goals. Depending on the project, you may need to interact with people in marketing, finance, operations, IT, and even human resources; you'll often get input from more than one department. The right way to approach data science is to start with a problem that has a bottom-line impact on your business and then work backward from the problem towards the analysis and the data needed to solve it. Insights don't happen in a vacuum; they come with the hard work of analyzing data and building models to solve real problems. Sometimes, the link between the business problem and the application of data science will be very clear, as in the case of correctly identifying fraudulent credit card transactions. In other cases, there can be multiple steps that separate the business problem from the data science application. The genesis and ultimate driving force for a data science project, more often than not, is based on a department-level need (e.g., finance, sales, marketing, etc.), and not the IT department, although they may need to provide you with the data set(s) you'll use for machine learning.

2. **Acquire the data set**: The data for analysis may come from a data warehouse or data mart. In some cases, the data may be an extract from a production system, e.g., an e-commerce application. More and more these days, the data for machine learning projects come from a variety of sources including unstructured sources such as social media or even e-mail. It is for this reason that data acquisition can require a degree of creativity on your part, again with the help of domain experts (like a controller, who may provide you with sales or commission data). This step may require involvement with the IT department, which may enlist the services of an extract-transform-load (ETL) engineer who can cut a data extract for you.

3. **Mung the data**: The task of data munging is very important early on in the project in order to clean and transform the raw data into a form more suitable to machine learning. Given the state of some enterprise data (dirty, inconsistent, missing values, etc.), this step may take considerable time and effort. It is important to document all the data munging steps you take as this process becomes part of your reusable data pipeline.

4. **Use exploratory data analysis**: Use statistical methods and plots to discover interesting characteristics and patterns in the data. Sometimes simple plots of raw data (or samples from raw data) can reveal very important insights that will help dictate a direction for the project or at least provide critical insight that can be useful when interpreting the results of the machine learning project.

5. **Perform feature engineering**: Use exploratory data analysis to determine the optimal feature variables to use for the particular machine learning algorithms you intend to employ for the project. This step may require discussions with domain experts about what surfaces during exploratory data analysis. Certainly, you'll need to fully understand the extent to which each feature variable may contribute to the prediction accuracy of the algorithm.

6. **Select the model**: Choose a machine learning algorithm appropriate for the problem being solved and split your data into training, cross validation, and test sets (more on this in Chapter 7). At this stage you need to make a commitment to the type of machine learning you'll use. Are you going to make a quantitative prediction, a qualitative classification, or are you just exploring using a clustering technique? After you gain experience with machine learning, you'll be able to more readily identify the algorithm most appropriate to use for a particular application.

7. **Validate the model**: There is no single algorithm that bests all others over all possible data sets. On a particular data set, one specific method may work best, while another method may work better on a different data set. Hence it is an important task to evaluate which method produces the best results for any given data set. Selecting the best

approach can be one of the most challenging parts of machine learning in practice. As a result, performance evaluation of a model is critical to the success of the project. We need to measure how well its predictions actually match the observed data; that is, we need to quantify the extent to which the predicted response value for a given observation is close to the true response value for that observation. We also need to determine the degree of overfitting that occurs, i.e., when a given algorithm yields a small training error but a large test set error. Specifically, we need to evaluate how well the model generalizes. Further, we need to diagnose bias vs. variance (a topic for Chapter 7), where we seek an algorithm that simultaneously achieves low variance and low bias.

8. **Visualize the data**: The final results of a machine learning project can best be understood with well-crafted visualizations that capture the essence of what the algorithm is telling us about the data. Visualizations that communicate the proper message are not easy to create and may require several tries to be successful. In fact, building effective visualizations requires a certain creative and artistic flair. Fortunately, the Internet is packed with plenty of examples of effective visualizations that you can use to come up with a direction for your own.

9. **Communicate the results**: Once you've completed the data science process, you're ready to communicate the results to the organization's decision makers. In order to be effective, you need to become a "data storyteller," someone who can tell a compelling tale based on what the data says. Realizing that most managers won't have a background in data analysis or statistics, it is your job to bring it all down to a form that is understandable by a typical business person. In order to take action on the results, the decision maker must truly understand what's being communicated—not in a data science sense, but rather in an actionable business intelligence sense. It's not easy, but telling the story of the data is an integral part of being a data scientist.

10. **Deploy to production**: Once the project is complete, an important next step is to deploy the machine learning solution in a production environment. The form this environment takes is dependent on the

goals for the project. If you're working on a recommender system, then deployment might mean adding functionality to an e-commerce website. If you're working on a churn rate predictor, then deployment might mean an addition to a marketing system. Or if you're working on a project to help close sales deals, then there might not be any sort of actual deployment, but rather a change in the sales department Standard Operating Procedure (SOP) document (e.g., continuing to call on potential customers after the seventh call is a point of diminishing returns). You'll also need special tools for deploying an R-based machine learning solution in a production environment. This subject is discussed later in this chapter.

Following the above guidelines, there are a number of important goals for any machine learning project. First, the algorithm's results should be interpretable; that is, the domain expert in the organization should be able to understand (with your help, of course) what the algorithm is saying about the data. Next, the results should be simple enough to explain clearly, as opposed to an overly complex solution; a lot of this depends on your ability to translate the technology into actionable business intelligence. Often you have some tradeoffs with respect to accuracy; namely, do you give up some accuracy in return for interpretability and simplicity? If you give up too much accuracy, then you may need to revisit the other factors (i.e., giving up a little simplicity to gain accuracy may be worthwhile). The algorithm also must be fast. This means it should be easy to build the model and easy to test it with small samples. Finally, the algorithm should be scalable, which means it should be easy to apply to a large data set, whether that means it is very fast or it is parallelizable across multiple samples.

MATHEMATICS BEHIND MACHINE LEARNING

In writing this book for the widest possible audience, I've made a conscious decision to leave out mathematics. I am not particularly excited about this decision because I'm convinced that a thorough understanding of machine learning principles requires a comprehension of the mathematical foundations of each algorithm. So although you can get by without math at this early period of your education, I fully expect that at some point you'll want to circle back to revisit each algorithm and dig into the math behind it. In my opinion, a mathematical basis is required to be a data scientist with a specialization in machine learning. The areas of mathematics you'll need to know include mathematical statistics, probability theory, calculus, linear algebra, partial differential equations, and combinatorics.

If you don't have a mathematics background from college, it's never too late to build that foundation. There are many resources available today to get up to speed with the mathematics of machine learning: *Massive Open Online Courses* (MOOCs) like Coursera, edX, MIT OpenCourseWare, and Kahn Academy. Searching YouTube for each of the areas of mathematics mentioned above will yield quality lectures for you to follow and learn from.

Once you obtain this mathematical perspective, you'll be in a position to answer the question that pops up more and more these days: "Is data science a real science?" My position on this matter is strongly affirmative! Data science is a confluence of disciplines, each of which is based on the areas of mathematics mentioned earlier. Using these principles, you can effectively apply the "scientific method" that I outlined in the Preface.

BECOMING A DATA SCIENTIST

In assessing your future professional plans around machine learning, you should consider the knowledge it takes to become a data scientist. You only need to review current job postings for the position to understand the diversity in stated requirements. Many companies are seeking candidates with backgrounds in mathematics, statistical modeling, algorithm design and validation, software engineering to build production systems, system architecture and administration, distributed computer systems (e.g., Hadoop and Spark), cloud solutions, storage systems, and domain experience. Plus, this person should be able to communicate experimental results to a C-level audience. Such candidates are called "unicorns," mythical creatures that don't exist in nature—or, in terms of the current discussion, a data science superhero. In reality, these kinds of job descriptions describe a team and not an individual, but many companies hold out for months or even more than a year to find their unicorn.

The various areas of data science mentioned above require dramatically different skills, education, and training with very little overlap. For example, suppose a company wants to locate outliers in millions of insurance claims to identify fraud. They would want someone experienced in sampling and multivariate statistical analysis. The company also might want to design and implement a software solution for use as a production system. Is this one person? Does a person with a Ph.D. in statistics also write code and design/configure hardware architectures? And conversely, does a software engineer do mathematical statistics? Not likely—these areas of responsibility are normally mutually exclusive.

What is more realistic is for you to decide up front whether you wish to be a *theorist* or an *experimentalist*. The theorist is someone who utilizes modest-sized data sets (or samples from large data stores) and performs formal data analysis, data munging, exploratory data analysis, model selection, and validation in order to establish the theoretical foundations for the project. This person should have a firm understanding of machine learning and the mathematical principles behind it. The experimentalist, on the other hand, is more of a software engineer or someone having experience building production software applications. This person should understand the mechanics of machine learning and how they can be deployed in production environments. This person might build Hadoop clusters, write MapReduce code, manage data storage hardware, write high-availability production code, and address the need for scalable hardware architectures.

Data science is defined to include all of these specialties, which makes life confusing for employers and applicants. If a company advertises for data scientist, do they expect someone who can do sophisticated statistical analysis and manipulate large data *and* design/build scalable software systems? It is true that many companies wanting to hire a data scientist are holding out for such a unicorn, but that would be like advertising for an architect to design a new building, but also expecting him/her to pour cement and nail two-by-fours together.

One solution is to educate employers and their HR team that they really need to hire a data science team by breaking up the "data scientist" position into specialties such as:

- Mathematics/statistics
- Computer science
- Software engineering
- Domain experience

The *Data Science Venn Diagram 2.0* shown in Figure 1-3 below is not meant to be a precise description of the overlap but only a graphic guideline. Notice that the unicorn central element represents a very rare intersection of all the disciplines.

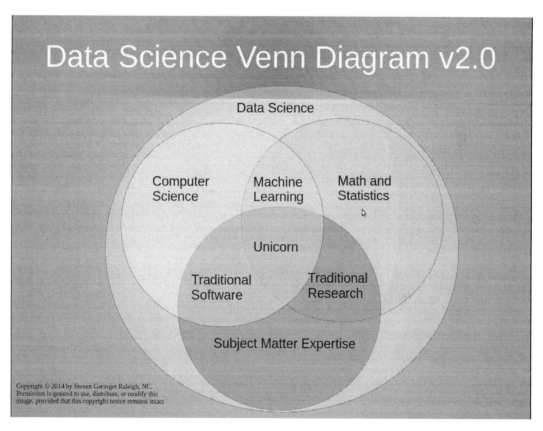

Figure 1-3 The Data Science Venn Diagram 2.0

R PROJECT FOR STATISTICAL COMPUTING

In the past several years, the R statistical environment has become of considerable importance to the machine language community. Although there are many choices for performing tasks related to data analysis, data modeling, and machine learning, R has become the overwhelming favorite among data scientists today. This is due to the extensive use of R in academia, rather than commercial products like SAS and SPSS. Currently, there are spirited debates between the R user community and both the SAS and Python communities as to the best tool for data scientists. R has compelling justifications including the availability of free, open source R; a widely used extensible language; around 7,000 packages available on CRAN to extend the functionality of R; top-rated visualization capabilities; and a thriving user community with the likes of blog consolidator r-bloggers.com.

Here is a short list of facts about R that demonstrate its popularity and growth:

1. R is the highest paid IT skill (Dice.com survey, January, 2014)

2. R is the most used data science language after SQL (O'Reilly survey, January, 2014)

3. R is used by 70% of data miners (Rexer survey, October, 2013)

4. R is #15 of all programming languages (RedMonk language rankings, January, 2014)

5. R is growing faster than any other data science language (KDNuggets survey, August, 2013)

6. R is the #1 Google Search for Advanced Analytics software (Google Trends, March, 2014)

7. R has more than two million users worldwide (Oracle estimate, February, 2012)

RSTUDIO

At this point, it may be instructive to provide a short overview of the RStudio IDE. I highly recommend that you use RStudio for your work with machine learning using R. Figure 1-4 below shows a typical RStudio session.

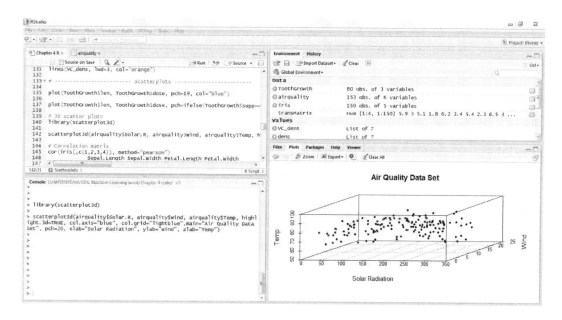

Figure 1-4 The RStudio integrated development environment

The RStudio screen is divided into four panes. The upper left pane is the R script editor, where you can type your R programming code into separate code files. You can have multiple code files open at once to copy code from one script to another. In order to run lines of R code, all you need to do is highlight the lines with your mouse and click on the Run tool in the editor's tool bar. When you run code, the lines will appear in the lower left pane, which is the R console. Each line is preceded with the ">" symbol. Here, you'll also see any effect of the code you run. For example, if you enter the following line in the console, you'll see the response of the calculation immediately afterward.

```
> mean(iris$Sepal.Length)

[1] 5.843333
```

In the top right pane, you'll see the Environment tab, which contains two sections: Data, showing all the active data sets, and Variables, showing all the program variables created by your R scripts. Note that if you click on a data set name, a new data browser appears in the upper left pane so you can scroll through data items found in the data set.

In the bottom right pane, you'll see a number of different tabs: Files, Plots, Packages, Help, and Viewer. The results of all plot features are directed to this pane. Help information is also directed to this pane. You can also see all the active packages in your R environment.

USING R PACKAGES

R embraces the open source paradigm in a very aggressive manner through use of so-called "packages" that extend the software's base functionality. There are a significant number of general purpose packages (currently around 7,000), many of them dealing with useful statistical methods, as well as domain-specific packages: finance, astronomy, molecular biology, ecology, and much more. You can always find the current number of R packages available by using the following R script:

```
> dim(available.packages())
```

R packages are contributed to *The Comprehensive R Archive Network* (CRAN) repository by experts from around the world. To find the CRAN URL closest to your geographical location, visit www.r-project.org, click on the CRAN link, and select your country/location. From there, you can see a page of available CRAN packages by name. It's a very long web page, so you'll need to use your browser's Find tool to search the list by keyword. For example, there are six packages with the keyword "finance" in the name. There are also private R packages not found in CRAN that you can locate using Google and then download and install into your local configuration.

Once you've found an R package suitable for your needs, you'll need to install it with your local R configuration. For example, here is how to install the lubridate package:

```
> install.packages("lubridate")
```

A package has to be installed only once. From then on, all you need to do is load it into memory using library(). The library() function is used to load libraries (groups of functions and data sets) that are not included in the base R distribution:

```
> library(lubridate)
```

Once you've installed a new package, you should visit the package's page on CRAN to download the Reference Manual and any Vignettes that may be available for the package. The Reference Manual contains a description and sample usage of each function available in the package including a complete list of arguments for each function. The manual, however, is for reference purposes only and is usually not a good resource for learning. A vignette is more like a tutorial or collection of use-case examples, and thus is very useful for learning about the features of the package and how to use them. Unfortunately, not all packages have vignettes.

More specific to the subject matter of this book, R is a treasure trove of machine learning resources. You'll find plenty of machine learning functionality in the base R distribution, plus numerous add-on packages for machine learning algorithms. For example, base R contains the `stats` package, which has commonly used algorithms such as `lm()` to fit a simple linear regression model, `glm()` for fitting generalized linear models such as logistic regression, `hclust()` for hierarchical clustering, `kmeans()` for k-means clustering, `prcomp()` for principal component analysis, and many more.

In addition, there are add-on packages for machine learning that supplement base R functionality, such as `knn()` in the `class` package for the K-nearest neighbors algorithm, `tree()` in the `tree` package to fit a classification tree or regression tree, `randomForest()` in the `randomForest` package for performing the random forests algorithm, `svm()` in the `e1071` package for support vector machines, and many more.

To find other R packages that suite your machine learning needs, you can simply use Google. For instance, if you wonder if there is a useful package that implements evolutionary algorithms, you can use the search term "evolutionary algorithms in r." This search yields a reference to the `DEoptim` package, which contains a useful machine learning algorithm.

DATA SETS

Since machine learning is all about data, and since this book endeavors to teach machine learning methods, it is natural that we will need a number of sample data sets to use in the examples throughout the book. To keep things simple—and not require you to download data sets from obscure locations that may go away over time—we'll use many of the example data sets that come with the R software base installation. To see a list of available data sets, use the following command:

```
> data()
```

The specific data sets you'll see listed depends on the packages you've installed and which packages you've loaded into memory. Packages routinely include data sets that you can use to test out the various functions residing in the package. To see the data sets accompanying a particular package, you can use the following command:

```
> data(package="plyr")
```

To learn more about a specific data set, you can use the ? command followed by the name of the data set, as shown in the example below. R will provide a brief description of the data set, the number of observations (examples), a list of variable names (features), code examples, and, in many cases, a description of each variable. Figure 1-5 shows the R help information for the airquality data set. We will use a number of well-known data sets in this book, and it is highly recommended that you become familiar with each variable in each data set.

```
> ? airquality
```

You can load a specific data set into memory using the following command:

```
> data(iris)
```

You'll see the name of the data set in the Workspace tab in RStudio.

airquality {datasets}

R Documentation

New York Air Quality Measurements

Description

Daily air quality measurements in New York, May to September 1973.

Usage

```
airquality
```

Format

A data frame with 154 observations on 6 variables.

```
[,1] Ozone    numeric Ozone (ppb)
[,2] Solar.R  numeric Solar R (lang)
[,3] Wind     numeric Wind (mph)
[,4] Temp     numeric Temperature (degrees F)
[,5] Month    numeric Month (1--12)
[,6] Day      numeric Day of month (1–31)
```

Details

Daily readings of the following air quality values for May 1, 1973 (a Tuesday) to September 30, 1973.

- `Ozone`: Mean ozone in parts per billion from 1300 to 1500 hours at Roosevelt Island

- `Solar.R`: Solar radiation in Langleys in the frequency band 4000–7700 Angstroms from 0800 to 1200 hours at

Figure 1-5 R help information for the `airquality` data set

USING R IN PRODUCTION

A natural question to ask once you've completed your machine learning project using R is whether you can now deploy your solution to a production environment. The answer is generally no; open source R is not a good option for production systems due to performance and memory limitations. This is especially true for Big Data machine learning projects that need to access extraordinarily large data sets. So rather than re-write everything in another language like C++ or Python, what are some alternatives? You could start by employing the `bigmemory` package, which allows you to create, store, access, and manipulate massive matrices. Then you could add these packages for advanced functionality: `biganalytics`, `bigalgebra`, `bigtabulate`, and `bigpca`. These packages may get you farther down the road toward a viable production system, but you're still likely to encounter roadblocks along the way.

Fortunately, there are a few commercial versions of R designed for use at the enterprise level. One is from Revolutions Analytics with their *Revolution R Enterprise* (RRE) offering. Another is from TIBCO, with their *TIBCO Enterprise Runtime for R* (TERR) offering. Both commercial versions provide optimized versions of familiar R machine learning algorithms that are designed to handle large amounts of data very quickly.

SUMMARY

In this chapter we worked to establish an introduction to the field of machine learning, also known as statistical learning. In addition, we set the stage for working on a data science project and provided a roadmap for the balance of the book. The first step in building a machine language solution is to explore ways to access data sets in a variety of common formats. In Chapter 2, we'll see many examples of data access that you can add to your data science toolbox.

Here is a summary of what you've learned in this chapter:

- We summarized the two types of machine learning we'll learn in this book: supervised learning and unsupervised learning.
- Using the Kaggle data science challenge website, we reviewed several real-life problems with a machine learning solution and also a number of categories of prospective problem domains.
- We examined the steps involved in the process of data science.
- We also commented on how you might become a practicing data scientist, as well as obtain the mathematical foundation you'll eventually need.
- This book is based on the R statistical environment, so we discussed this important tool and how to use it for machine learning, along with the RStudio IDE.
- We discussed the power of R packages in doing machine learning and saw how to utilize the data sets that accompany many R packages.
- Finally, we commented on using R in a production environment, which is the ultimate goal of many projects.

Chapter 2
Data Access

Data science, and its enabling technology machine learning, is all about data—making predictions about future events using vast amounts of data to train predictive algorithms and also sifting through data stores to detect patterns that are of strategic value to the organization. So naturally, an important part of the machine learning process is accessing data content from disparate sources that is pertinent to the problem being solved. Many machine learning and data analysis discussions make the assumption that you already have a clean data set ready, waiting for you to apply exploratory data analysis techniques and select an appropriate machine learning model. Unfortunately, this is rarely the case. Much more often, you need to locate the data, determine in what format it resides, find an R package that includes functions for accessing the data, and finally, access the data and read it into an R data frame—all topics for this chapter. This process sets the stage for the next important step, data munging, which is the subject of Chapter 3.

Let's take a step back and propose a definition of "data" as follows:

> *Data are values of qualitative or quantitative variables belonging to a population; the set of objects you're interested in where a variable is a measurement of characteristic of an item.*

Examples of a population are sales data for a product, ad response data, and manufacturing process data. Examples of qualitative variables are gender, country, and department, while examples of quantitative variables are sales price, number of clicks for an ad, and quantity of product manufactured in one hour. The goal for the data access phase of a machine learning project is to locate and secure data sources that yield support for the problem domain.

The importance of the data access step in a machine learning project cannot be minimized. If there's one thing I've learned from working with organizations on machine learning projects, it's that people have an innate compulsion to squirrel away data that can serve the data science process in multiple locations and multiple formats. In a sense, it is this lack of proper data governance that requires us to be nimble in our abilities to read data from whatever the source. Whether you work at a startup company, large enterprise, or academic institution, you'll want to master a broad variety of techniques for accessing data sets.

There's never been a point in time when the amount of available data and our ability to learn from that data has been greater. The so-called "big data" industry is capitalizing on the rise of diverse sources of data in a significant way. The variety and depth of data sources keeps increasing; a good example of this direction is the increased use of unstructured social media data, where sentiment and credibility can be derived and coupled with transactional data sets to achieve unprecedented levels of predictive capabilities.

The goal for this chapter is to provide you with a useful data access toolset you can reuse over and over again for subsequent machine learning projects. The data access processes you'll learn here will become the first stage of your data pipeline which will be discussed in Chapter 3. When a data scientist encounters an entirely new data source type, she must research import mechanisms (similar to those we present here) and add it to the methods from this chapter. Over time, you'll have a toolset growing in functionality to embrace most common data sources. The advantage of an open source tool like R is that given time, someone will develop a new package to handle a data source that is growing in popularity. This is exactly what happened with Twitter.

In this chapter, we'll examine a number of ways to access a wide cross section of data content and pull it into the R environment to be used as input to learning algorithms. This process represents the first step in the machine learning equation. Here's a list of topics for this chapter:

- Managing your R data work environment
- Types and sources of data sets
- Downloading data sets from the web
- Reading data files: CSV, Excel, JSON
- Scraping web pages for data content
- Accessing data using SQL
- SQL equivalents in R

- Reading Twitter data
- Reading Google Analytics data
- Writing data

MANAGING YOUR WORKING DIRECTORY

When starting a new machine learning project in R, a basic component is deciding where to store your work. A *working directory* is a place on your computer's hard drive in which to store various files comprising the project: data files, R scripts, plot image files, .RDATA file, as well as files to document your analysis (Word, PowerPoint, etc.). Some people use a subfolder called "data" underneath the working directory just to store the data files.

Once you've created the working directory, you must manage its location from within the R environment. R has two commands to manage the working directory: getwd() retrieves the current working directory, and setwd() sets the working directory. Upon starting RStudio, you can set the working directory from the R console with the setwd() function using the relative paths method:

```
> setwd("./MYPROJECT")
> getwd()
[1] "C:/Users/Dan/MYPROJECT"
```

Using the absolute paths method, you can use the following syntax:

```
> setwd("/Users/dan/MYPROJECT")
> getwd()
[1] "C:/Users/dan/MYPROJECT"
```

If you're using Windows like I am and wish to use the Windows syntax for specifying pathnames using the backslash ("\"), you need to use the special syntax of a double backslash ("\\"), as in the following:

```
> setwd("C:\\Users\\Dan\\MYPROJECT")
> getwd()
[1] "C:/Users/Dan/MYPROJECT"
```

Another way to manage your working directory is to use the RStudio feature: `Session -> Set Working Directory -> Choose Directory` to point to the directory you desire.

As you're working on your machine learning project, it is a good idea to frequently save your work to a Workspace file saved in your working directory. The easiest way to do this is through RStudio, using: `Session -> Save Workspace As` and then enter a file name for your Workspace file, usually the name of your project such as `MYPROJECT.RData`. A Workspace file saves the current state of your work environment, including data values and data sets. Later, when loading RStudio again, you can open R with the same Workspace file to restore your current state so you can continue working where you left off. Each project you're working on should have its own working directory and Workspace file.

TYPES OF DATA FILES

There are many potential types of files that can be used as machine learning data sets. It is the job of the data scientist to have the tools needed to import data sets from disparate sources and coalesce them into a uniform structure inside the R environment. Subsequent sections of this chapter will focus on specific data source types and demonstrate how to load the data into memory in the form of an R data frame. Once in a data frame, the often lengthy data munging process can commence. Here is a list of the types of data files we'll consider in this chapter:

- Comma separated values (CSV) files
- Excel files
- JSON files
- HTML pages
- SQL databases
- Twitter
- Google Analytics

SOURCES OF DATA

You'll find that there are many potential sources of data files used for machine learning projects. In all likelihood, you'll obtain the data set from a domain expert in the organization for which you're working. This could be an IT person who was asked to provide you with the data set, it could be a person from the finance department who keeps distilled subsets of the company's data warehouse in Excel, or it could be a consultant who manages the social media effort for the organization. Here is a list of other sources:

- Machine learning data repository on the web: Some widely known repositories include the UC Irvine Machine Learning Repository (archive.ics.uci.edu/ml), government data websites (such as data.gov), and the machine learning challenge website Kaggle (www.kaggle.com).

- From an application programming interface (API): The most common API used for social media data is the Twitter API, but there are many others. With Google, you can easily research if other social media platforms have an API for use with R (via a special package).

- By scraping a web page: Just about any website you might come across can be used as a data source, especially if it displays data content in an organized manner. The only caveat here is that you'll need a URL that can be used from R to render a web page containing the data. The section in this chapter on scraping data from web pages will demonstrate this approach.

As you continue to learn the principles of machine learning, you should always be on the lookout for new sources of data and engage this thought process: How can I extract knowledge, and therefore value, from this data set through use of machine learning algorithms?

DOWNLOADING DATA SETS FROM THE WEB

As mentioned in the previous section, there are many sources of data for machine learning on the web that make data sets available for download. One useful class of data made available to the general public is government data.

To demonstrate how to download data from the web, we'll use the *San Francisco Data* website (data.sfgov.org) as shown in Figure 2-1, which contains a wide variety of municipal data sets. We'll use the *Parking Meter* data set that includes various meter characteristics. Our goal is to download the data set in CSV file format directly from the website. To do this, we'll use the `download.file()` command. Note that not all data available on the web will be in a nice structured format, i.e., where each row contains variables associated with a single observation. Often, the data you find on the web requires significant re-working to get it into a form that's proper for data analysis and machine learning.

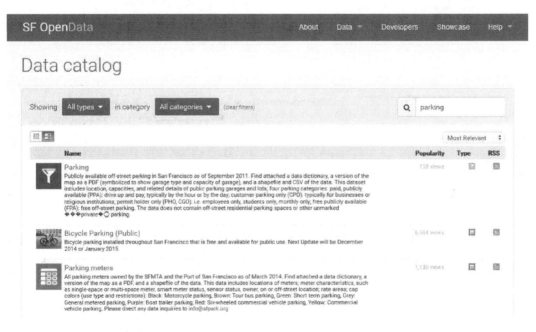

Figure 2-1 Example data source – San Francisco Data, data.sfgov.org

The following code defines a variable `fileURL` and assigns to it the URL (web address) of the data set. The URL was obtained from the San Francisco Data website. Next, the `download.file()` command is used to download the file and places it in the `data` subfolder underneath the working directory. The `list.files()` function is then used to confirm the download was completed. Notice the use of a relative path, `./data`, which refers to a subfolder underneath the current working directory.

```
> fileURL <- "https://data.sfgov.org/api/views/7egw-
    qt89/rows.csv?accessType=DOWNLOAD"
> download.file(fileURL, destfile="./data/SFParkingMeters.csv")
> list.files("./data")
[1] "SFParkingMeters.csv"
```

The next step is to read the data set into a data frame using the read.table() function. Then we can take a look at the first few rows using head() to see if the data arrived in good form while also becoming familiar with the data elements:

```
> SFParkingMeters <-
    read.table("./data/SFParkingMeters.csv",sep=",", header=TRUE)
> head(SFParkingMeters)
```

	POST_ID	MS_ID	MS_SPACEID	CAP_COLOR	METER_TYPE	SMART_METE	ACTIVESENS
1	354-20160	-	0.0	Grey	SS	Y	Y
2	354-21030	-	0.0	Green	SS	Y	Y
3	354-21160	-	0.0	Yellow	SS	Y	Y
4	363-05250	-	0.0	Grey	SS	N	N
5	363-05270	-	0.0	Grey	SS	N	N
6	464-04120	-	0.0	Grey	SS	Y	Y

	JURISDICTI	ON_OFF_STR	OSP_ID	STREET_NUM	STREETNAME	STREET_SEG	RATEAREA
1	SFMTA	ON	0.0	2016.0	CHESTNUT ST	3977000.0	Area 5
2	SFMTA	ON	0.0	2103.0	CHESTNUT ST	3979000.0	Area 5
3	SFMTA	ON	0.0	2116.0	CHESTNUT ST	3979000.0	Area 5
4	SFMTA	ON	0.0	525.0	COLUMBUS AVE	4295000.0	Area 3
5	SFMTA	ON	0.0	527.0	COLUMBUS AVE	4295000.0	Area 3
6	SFMTA	ON	0.0	412.0	HAYES ST	6816000.0	Area 5

	SFPARKAREA	LOCATION
1	Marina	(37.800798, -122.43687)
2	Marina	(37.800522, -122.438067)
3	Marina	(37.800589, -122.438525)
4		(37.800053, -122.409985)
5		(37.800088, -122.410035)
6	Civic Center	(37.776878, -122.423512)

READING CSV FILES

The most common type of data file you're likely to encounter is the comma separated value (CSV) type of file. This is because CSV is like the lingua franca of the data science community, and many software applications export to CSV. Similarly, most software applications and environments (like R) are able to read CSV. If you're unfamiliar with what a CSV file actually looks like, just open it up in a tool like Windows Notepad. The format of a CSV file is simple: each line (row) in the file represents a single observation, and each column represents a variable (potential feature variable). R can handle the case where the first row contains a list of variable names and also the case where this first row is missing (in which case R will assign arbitrary variable names which you can rename later).

Your first step, once you've received the CSV file, is to place it in your working directory. In order to read the contents of the CSV into memory for use by R, you can use the `read.table()` function, which is the general way that R offers to read a file in tabular format, not necessarily in CSV format. The `read.csv()` function is essentially identical to `read.table()` except that it only reads the CSV format, typically exported by spreadsheet applications like Excel. In either case, the file is read into a data frame object. To demonstrate this, we'll read in the Parking Meter data set from the previous section.

```
> SFParkingMeters <- read.csv("./data/SFParkingMeters.csv")
```

Once you've successfully read in the file, you can display its contents in RStudio either by clicking the data frame name `SFParkingMeters` in the Workspace pane or by entering the command `view(SFParketingMeters)` in the console. Figure 2-2 depicts what you will see. You can browse through the data just as you would in a spreadsheet; however, it is non-editable. Notice that this data set has 29,253 observations and 16 variables. If you just want to view the first six rows of the data frame, you can also use `head(SFParkingMeters)`.

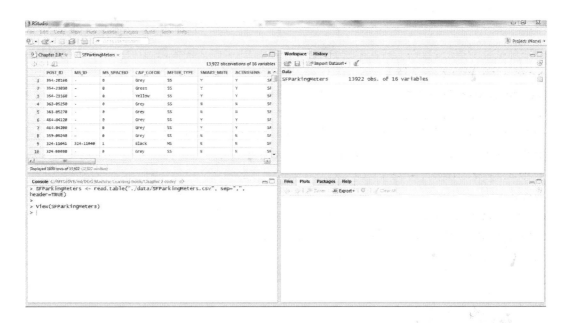

Figure 2-2 Viewing the data set using RStudio

Another useful way to read in a file is with the file.choose() function, which can be embedded in read.table() or read.csv(). This method of reading in a file will prompt you with a dialog box to point to the file on your computer.

```
> SFParkingMeters <- read.csv(file.choose())
```

READING EXCEL FILES

Another important file type for machine learning is Excel. Excel is a universally used spreadsheet application and all sizes of organizations depend on this tool to store business information. It is therefore understandable that the data you may wish to use for machine learning resides in Excel. An important requirement is that Excel files contain only simple rows and columns of data.

R provides a method of reading data directly from an Excel 2007 spreadsheet file using the read.xlsx() and read.xlsx2() functions. The read.xlsx2() function is generally faster for large spreadsheets. To test reading an Excel file, we need to return to the San Francisco Data website and download the same Parking Meters data set, but this time in XLSX format. Note that since an Excel file is a binary file rather than plain text, we need to specify the `mode="wb"` argument (specifying the file is in binary format) for the `download.file()` function. We also need to use the `library()` function to load the `xlsx` package, otherwise the functions in the package will not be found when you use them. Finally, to read the Excel file into a data frame, we use `read.xlsx2()` with the `sheetIndex=1` argument indicating which sheet of the Excel file to read.

```
> fileUrl <- "https://data.sfgov.org/api/views/7egw-
    qt89/rows.xlsx?accessType=DOWNLOAD"
> download.file(fileUrl, destfile="./data/SFParkingMeters.xlsx",
    mode="wb")
> library(xlsx)
> SFParkingMeters <- read.xlsx2("./data/SFParkingMeters.xlsx",
    sheetIndex=1)
```

At this point, the end result should be the same as with the CSV file read in the previous section; namely, the data are loaded into the `SFParkingMeters` data frame. Note that many business users of Excel use this tool in a free form manner with much variation in the content of the spreadsheet, rather than simple rows and columns. In order to read an Excel spreadsheet into R, you may need to massage the data inside of Excel to simplify its structure.

USING FILE CONNECTIONS

Another way to read information from a data source is via a file connection. With a connection, you can read in a CSV file, for example, in a manner similar to what we've seen previously, but you can also read lines from a text file. Reading individual lines from a text file may make sense when the data are less structured. R has a useful function for this purpose, `readLines()`, which is used with a file connection. Before we see an example of `readLines()`, let's first see how connections work. Consider the sample code:

```
> con <- file("./data/SFParkingMeters.csv", "r")
> SFParkingMeters <- read.csv(con)
```

```
> close(con)
> head(SFParkingMeters)
```

The above example starts by using the `file()` function to establish a connection to the CSV file with the object we've named `con`. Then we call the `read.csv()` function using the connection object as an argument in order to read the contents of the file. Finally, it is considered good practice to always close connections when done with them. As before, the data frame `SFParkingMeters` contains the contents of the file.

Now let's go back to the `readLines()` function and do something entirely different. This time, the data source will be a web page, so we'll use the `url()` function to provide the address of the web page. We follow the same procedure as before but only read the first 20 lines of the page with the n=20 argument (to just read one line at a time, use n=1).

```
> con <- url("http://radicaldatascience.wordpress.com/", "r")
> RDS <- readLines(con, n=20)
> close(con)
> head(RDS)
```

Using `head()`, above, shows the HTML text we just read from my blog website's homepage.

```
[1] "<!DOCTYPE html>"          "<!--[if IE 7]>"
[3] "<html id=\"ie7\" lang=\"en\">" "<![endif]-->"
[5] "<!--[if IE 8]>"           "<html id=\"ie8\" lang=\"en\">"
```

One important aspect of using readLines() is that the lines are stored in a character vector instead of a data frame. You can check this by using the `class()` function:

```
> class(RDS)
[1] "character"
```

Having text lines from a file stored in a vector means you will have to write R code to process the data to interpret what the lines say. For example, if the lines contain Twitter social media content, then you may wish to develop an algorithm to perform sentiment analysis on the Tweets.

There are many other functions in R that deal with connections. In order to see a complete list, use this:

```
> ? connection
```

READING JSON FILES

Another data file type that you may encounter when reading data for a machine learning project is called JSON, or *JavaScript Object Notation*. JSON is a text-based open standard designed for human readable data interchange and is often used with Ajax web programming techniques that have become quite popular. R has two popular packages that are able to access JSON data files: `rjson` and `RJSONIO`. `rjson` does not use R's S4/S3 methods, so it is not readily extensible. It also does not use vectorized operations, making it too slow for non-trivial data. Similarly, for reading JSON data into R, `rjson` is somewhat slow and does not scale to large data. Consequently, we will use `RJSONIO` for this section.

We provide a data access example of reading a JSON file into R by first requesting a special URL for downloading the JSON version of the SFParkingMeters data set (JSON is another file type provided by the San Francisco Data website). Most of the work is done by the `fromJSON()` function that is found in the `RJSONIO` package. This function converts JSON data content into R objects for further analysis.

The R code below starts by saving the JSON URL in a variable, `fileURL`. Next, we refer to the URL in the `fromJSON()` function, which returns the data in a nested list object consisting of two primary components: `meta` and `data`. We will only need the `data` component, so we'll store that in the list object `parkdata`. The trick here is to know how to unravel the nested list into individual values for the variables. To do this, you need to take a peek at one observation using `parkdata[[1]]` and try to recognize some values, then note the index of those values so that they can be referenced in order to construct a data frame. We can use the list processing function `sapply()` to pull out data from the list. Lastly, we need to build a new data frame, park_df, containing three variables from the original JSON file: CAP_COLOR, METER_TYPE, STREETNAME. Now that the JSON data are in convenient data frame form, we can perform the usual analysis on the data.

```
> library(RJSONIO)
> fileURL <- "https://data.sfgov.org/api/views/7egw-
    qt89/rows.json?accessType=DOWNLOAD"
> parkdata <- fromJSON(fileURL)[[2]]
> park_df = data.frame(
  CAP_COLOR = sapply(parkdata, function(x) x[[12]]),
  METER_TYPE = sapply(parkdata, function(x) x[[13]]),
  STREETNAME = sapply(parkdata, function(x) x[[20]])
)
> head(park_df)
    CAP_COLOR    METER_TYPE    STREETNAME
1   Grey         SS            CHESTNUT ST
2   Green        SS            CHESTNUT ST
3   Yellow       SS            CHESTNUT ST
4   Grey         SS            COLUMBUS AVE
5   Grey         SS            COLUMBUS AVE
6   Grey         SS            HAYES ST
```

[handwritten annotation: "list convert to dframe"]

SCRAPING DATA FROM WEBSITES

It may seem strange to think of a website as a data source, but once you remember that a website is nothing more than a set of HTML documents and that HTML can represent data quite well, then the process of "reading" a website seems much more realistic. This technique is particularly useful for accessing data that is not readily available for downloading as a CSV file or other file types. Instead, we can "scrape" the data directly from the web page(s).

To demonstrate this data acquisition technique, let's take a look at a website containing a data set we'd like to pull into R for analysis. Figure 2-3 below contains manufacturing data Purchasing Managers Index (PMI) history. The goal is to write an R script to read the data directly from the web page and then load it into a data frame for further analysis. We'll take it one step further by morphing the data into a form more useable for our purposes.

	JAN	FEB	MAR	APR	MAY	JUN	JUL	AUG	SEP	OCT	NOV	DEC
2014	51.3											
2013	52.3	53.1	51.5	50.0	50.0	52.5	54.9	56.3	56.0	56.6	57.0	56.5
2012	52.8	52.4	53.0	53.7	53.2	51.0	50.6	51.1	52.2	51.2	49.5	50.4
2011	59.0	59.3	59.1	58.9	53.7	56.6	52.9	53.0	52.8	51.8	52.1	53.1
2010	57.2	55.8	58.8	58.1	58.3	56.4	56.4	58.0	56.3	57.7	57.6	57.5
2009	34.9	35.5	36.0	39.5	41.7	45.8	49.9	53.5	54.4	56.0	54.4	55.3
2008	50.3	47.6	48.3	48.8	48.8	49.8	50.0	49.2	44.8	38.9	36.5	33.1
2007	49.5	51.9	50.7	52.6	52.5	52.6	52.4	50.9	51.0	51.1	50.5	49.0
2006	55.0	55.8	54.3	55.2	53.7	52.0	53.0	53.7	52.2	51.4	50.3	51.4
2005	56.8	55.5	55.2	52.2	50.8	52.4	52.8	52.4	56.8	57.2	56.7	55.1
2004	60.8	59.9	60.6	60.6	61.4	60.5	59.9	58.5	57.4	56.3	56.2	57.2
2003	51.3	48.8	46.3	46.1	49.0	49.0	51.0	53.2	52.4	55.2	58.4	60.1
2002	47.5	50.7	52.4	52.4	53.1	53.6	50.2	50.3	50.5	49.0	48.5	51.6
2001	42.3	42.1	43.1	42.7	41.3	43.2	43.5	46.3	46.2	40.8	44.1	45.3
2000	56.7	55.8	54.9	54.7	53.2	51.4	52.5	49.9	49.7	48.7	48.5	43.9
1999	50.6	51.7	52.4	52.3	54.3	55.8	53.6	54.8	57.0	57.2	58.1	57.8
1998	53.8	52.9	52.9	52.2	50.9	48.9	49.2	49.3	48.7	48.7	48.2	46.8
1997	53.8	53.1	53.8	53.7	56.1	54.9	57.7	56.3	53.9	56.4	55.7	54.5
1996	45.5	45.9	46.9	49.3	49.1	53.6	49.7	51.6	51.1	50.5	53.0	55.2
1995	57.4	55.1	52.1	51.5	46.7	45.9	50.7	47.1	48.1	46.7	45.9	46.2
1994	56.0	56.5	56.9	57.4	58.2	58.8	58.5	58.0	59.0	59.4	59.2	56.1
1993	55.8	55.2	53.5	50.2	51.2	49.6	50.2	50.7	50.8	53.4	53.8	55.6
1992	47.3	52.7	54.6	52.6	55.7	53.6	53.9	53.4	49.7	50.3	53.6	54.2
1991	39.2	39.4	40.7	42.8	44.5	50.3	50.6	52.9	54.9	53.1	49.5	46.8
1990	47.2	49.1	49.9	50.0	49.5	49.2	46.6	46.1	44.5	43.2	41.3	40.8
1989	54.7	54.1	51.5	52.2	49.3	47.3	45.9	45.1	46.0	46.8	46.8	47.4
1988	57.5	56.2	54.6	55.8	55.5	59.3	58.2	56.0	54.6	55.5	55.6	56.0
1987	54.9	52.6	55.0	55.5	57.2	57.4	57.5	59.3	60.1	60.7	58.8	61.0

Figure 2-3 A web page from which we wish to scrape data

The code below begins by loading two packages: XML and reshape2. The XML package contains a function that is very useful for the scraping of web pages, readHTMLTable(), which extracts data from HTML tables in an HTML document (web page). An HTML table is frequently how data are represented on the web. This function returns the data in a list, which we then convert to a data frame for easier use. Using head(df) shows how the data now in a data frame is identical to what was on the web page.

```
> library(XML)
> library(reshape2)
> webdata <-
    readHTMLTable('http://www.ism.ws/ISMReport/content.cfm?ItemNumbe
    r=10752')
> df <- data.frame(webdata[[1]])
> names(df)[1] <- 'Year' # Add a name for first column
> head(df)
  Year JAN  FEB  MAR  APR  MAY  JUN  JUL  AUG  SEP  OCT  NOV  DEC
1 2014 51.3
2 2013 52.3 53.1 51.5 50.0 50.0 52.5 54.9 56.3 56.0 56.6 57.0 56.5
3 2012 52.8 52.4 53.0 53.7 53.2 51.0 50.6 51.1 52.2 51.2 49.5 50.4
4 2011 59.0 59.3 59.1 58.9 53.7 56.6 52.9 53.0 52.8 51.8 52.1 53.1
5 2010 57.2 55.8 58.8 58.1 58.3 56.4 56.4 58.0 56.3 57.7 57.6 57.5
6 2009 34.9 35.5 36.0 39.5 41.7 45.8 49.9 53.5 54.4 56.0 54.4 55.3
```

Let's take one more step at refining the data we scraped from the web page. We can use the `reshape2` package's `melt()` function, which is very powerful in how it can quickly transform a data frame. In this case, we take the tabular format that was read in from the web and reshape it to become ordered triples of `Year`, `Month`, and `PMI`. We also need to convert `PMI` to numeric and remove the observations where the `PMI` value is `NA` (for months where there was no `PMI` defined).

```
> df <- melt(df,id.vars='Year')
> names(df) <- c('Year','Month','PMI')
> df$PMI <- as.numeric(df$PMI)
> df <- na.omit(PMI)
```

SQL DATABASES

A common source of enterprise data is a SQL database. SQL databases are the lifeblood of businesses large and small. Many times data are stored in an enterprise-wide data warehouse or departmental data mart. Although the application of SQL databases is quite broad, the common thread is that data are stored in "tables," each consisting of rows and columns. Most database software applications, in fact, keep the data in multiple joined tables. The goal of utilizing SQL data in machine learning is to write new SQL queries (or use existing ones) to yield a single flat file containing the data you wish to use in your analysis. Since most SQL databases possess tools for exporting data to CSV files, using the techniques in the above sections to read CSV files written by the SQL database software is a valid option. (But you may decide that reading data directly from a SQL database is more attractive.)

The good news about accessing data content residing in a SQL database is that R has drivers for nearly every conceivable database. This is made possible through various R packages. Even if you're using a database that doesn't have a standalone driver, you can always use a generic ODBC (Open Database Connectivity) connection. Here is a short list of the more popular SQL database R packages available:

- RMySQL
- RMongo
- ROracle
- RPostgresSQL
- RSQLite
- RODBC

In order to demonstrate the process of reading data from a SQL database, I shall use an implementation I happen to have handy. Back in 2012, I was experimenting with some data sets for the famed Heritage Health Network machine learning competition on Kaggle.com and was using Microsoft SQL Server 2012 Express, a free version of Microsoft's enterprise relational database. I chose to read all the raw data files into SQL tables and then do much of the data munging (our topic for Chapter 3) inside of SQL Server. I used a large number of stored procedures to manage this process, which I would recommend for the purpose of performing complex joins, although intricate data transformations are best done in the R environment.

Here is a summary of how I established a connection to the SQL database, executed a simple SELECT query to pull data from a table, and then stored the data in an R data frame. These steps apply to the SQL database and development environment I used: namely, SQL Server 2012 Express running on a Windows 7 Professional laptop. You'll have to investigate the details for the SQL database and development environment you're using, but these steps should at least give you some familiarity with the process. Since SQL Server does not have its own R package, I used the RODBC package.

1. Created a User DSN (data source name) using the ODBC Data Source Administrator tool available in the Window Control Panel under Administrative Tools. I assigned the name "Heritage" to the User DSN.

2. Loaded the RODBC library.

3. Used the odbcConnect() function to establish a connection to the database using the "Heritage" DSN.

4. Passed a SQL SELECT query to the database, executed it using the sqlQuery() function, and then saved the result set in a data frame.

5. Closed the connection.

Here is the R code that achieves all this. At the end, we display all the variable names in the resulting data frame and perform and calculate the mean of a selected variable, PayDelayI, to show that the data coming from the SQL database is intact.

```
> library(RODBC)
> con <- odbcConnect("Heritage", uid="dan")
> df <- sqlQuery(con, "SELECT TOP 1000 [MemberID]
    ,[ProviderID]
    ,[Vendor]
          ,[PCP]
          ,[Year]
          ,[Specialty]
          ,[PlaceSvc]
          ,[PayDelay]
          ,[LengthOfStay]
          ,[DSFS]
          ,[PrimaryConditionGroup]
```

```
        ,[CharlsonIndex]
        ,[ProcedureGroup]
        ,[SupLOS]
        ,[dsfsI]
        ,[CharlsonIndexI]
        ,[LengthOfStayI]
        ,[PayDelayI]
        FROM [Heritage].[dbo].[Claims]")
> odbcClose(con)
> names(df)
 [1]  "MemberID"         "ProviderID"            "Vendor"
 [4]  "PCP"              "Year"                  "Specialty"
 [7]  "PlaceSvc"         "PayDelay"              "LengthOfStay"
[10]  "DSFS"             "PrimaryConditionGroup" "CharlsonIndex"
[13]  "ProcedureGroup"   "SupLOS"                "dsfsI"
[16]  "CharlsonIndexI"   "LengthOfStayI"         "PayDelayI"
> mean(df$PayDelayI)
[1]  42.944
```

While we're speaking of SQL databases and R, it is worthwhile to take a small detour here to demonstrate how you can perform SQL queries on your R data frames. If you're adept with SQL, you may find using SQL for accessing data content in R more palatable than using some of the more terse data munging tools available in R (many of which we'll see in Chapter 3). The key to using SQL inside of R is the sqldf package, which allows you to treat data frames like SQL tables and reference them in standard SQL syntax. Even if you've never used SQL, you may be interested in this capability since using SQL lends some ease of use to otherwise difficult R language constructs.

Let's see an example of using SQL inside of R. Here is a typical business application of orders and products. Instead of referencing an existing data set, we'll just create some test data on the fly by creating two data frames, orders and product. The orders data frame has three variables: order_no, prod_id and qty, representing the order number, product ID and quantity of an order, respectively. The product data frame also has three variables:

product_id, desc, and price, representing the product ID, description, and price of a product, respectively. We'd like to use a SQL join query to relate the two data frames by the common key prod_id, and then create a new data frame containing the result set consisting of order_no, prod_id, qty, and price.

```
> orders <-
    data.frame(order_no=c("10021","10022","10023","10024","10025"),
    prod_id=c("AC-01","AC-01","AD-11","AE-21","AM-19"),
    qty=c(1,1,2,3,1))
> product <- data.frame(prod_id=c("AC-01","AD-11","AE-21","AM-
    19","AG-40"), desc=c("Widget A","Widget B","Widget C","Widget
    D", "Widget E"), price=c(123.50,25,55,17.95,45.33))
> sqldf("SELECT o.*, p.price FROM orders o INNER JOIN product p ON
    o.prod_id = p.prod_id;")
```

	order_no	prod_id	qty	price
1	10021	AC-01	1	123.50
2	10022	AC-01	1	123.50
3	10023	AD-11	2	25.00
4	10024	AE-21	3	55.00
5	10025	AM-19	1	17.95

SQL EQUIVALENTS IN R

R has a number of ways to access data sets stored in data frames that are similar to the functionality in SQL. If you already know SQL, it is useful to see the R methods for manipulating data that have equivalent SQL commands. In this section, we'll see a number of techniques that will come in handy when accessing data. To illustrate these techniques, we'll use the CO2 data set that is available in the base R system. Let's take a look at the structure and content of this data set:

```
> data(CO2)
> head(CO2)
```

	Plant	Type	Treatment	conc	uptake
1	Qn1	Quebec	nonchilled	95	16.0

2	Qn1	Quebec	nonchilled	175	30.4
3	Qn1	Quebec	nonchilled	250	34.8
4	Qn1	Quebec	nonchilled	350	37.2
5	Qn1	Quebec	nonchilled	500	35.3
6	Qn1	Quebec	nonchilled	675	39.2

The CO2 data set consists of 84 observations and five variables: Plant, Type, Treatment, conc, and uptake. One of the first things you typically do with a data set is to select rows based on a filter. Here is the SQL SELECT statement to retrieve records from the data frame based on a filtered condition and create a new subset data frame:

```
SELECT * FROM CO2 WHERE conc>400 AND uptake>40
```
Sql

The R equivalent uses the following simple syntax:

```
CO2_subset <- CO2[CO2$conc>400 & CO2$uptake>40,]
head(CO2_subset)
```
R simple subsetting

	Plant	Type	Treatment	conc	uptake
12	Qn2	Quebec	nonchilled	500	40.6
13	Qn2	Quebec	nonchilled	675	41.4
14	Qn2	Quebec	nonchilled	1000	44.3
19	Qn3	Quebec	nonchilled	500	42.9
20	Qn3	Quebec	nonchilled	675	43.9
21	Qn3	Quebec	nonchilled	1000	45.5

```
> dim(CO2_subset)    # 8 observations selected
[1] 8 5
```

Next, we'll see an example of the SQL SELECT statement's ORDER BY clause. Here, we wish to sort the result set by the variable conc (ascending sequence) and then by the variable uptake (descending sequence). Here is the SQL statement:

```
SELECT * FROM CO2 ORDER BY conc, uptake DESC
```

The R equivalent uses the following simple syntax. (I've added some additional R syntax to limit the result set to the first 20 records, but this is only for convenience here since I didn't want to display all 84 observations from the CO_2 data set.)

— sign = descending? (handwritten)

```
> CO2[order(CO2$conc, -CO2$uptake),][1:20,]
```

↓ (handwritten)

	Plant	Type	Treatment	conc	uptake
15	Qn3	Quebec	nonchilled	95	16.2
1	Qn1	Quebec	nonchilled	95	16.0
36	Qc3	Quebec	chilled	95	15.1
22	Qc1	Quebec	chilled	95	14.2
8	Qn2	Quebec	nonchilled	95	13.6
50	Mn2	Mississippi	nonchilled	95	12.0
57	Mn3	Mississippi	nonchilled	95	11.3
43	Mn1	Mississippi	nonchilled	95	10.6
78	Mc3	Mississippi	chilled	95	10.6
64	Mc1	Mississippi	chilled	95	10.5
29	Qc2	Quebéc	chilled	95	9.3
71	Mc2	Mississippi	chilled	95	7.7
16	Qn3	Quebec	nonchilled	175	32.4
2	Qn1	Quebec	nonchilled	175	30.4
9	Qn2	Quebec	nonchilled	175	27.3
30	Qc2	Quebec	chilled	175	27.3
23	Qc1	Quebec	chilled	175	24.1
51	Mn2	Mississippi	nonchilled	175	22.0
37	Qc3	Quebec	chilled	175	21.0
58	Mn3	Mississippi	nonchilled	175	19.4

Another powerful SQL construct is the GROUP BY clause used to compute aggregate values such as average. In this case, we'd like to calculate the average uptake value for each unique value of Plant. Here is the SQL statement to achieve this:

```
SELECT Plant, AVG(uptake) FROM CO2 GROUP BY Plant
```

The R equivalent uses the following syntax based on the aggregate function, which drives the process. The first argument, x, for aggregate() is CO2[,c("uptake")], which isolates the uptake column from the CO2 data frame. The second argument, by is data.frame(CO2$Plant), which is the grouping variable. Finally, the FUN argument is the R function, which is used to compute summary statistics—in this case, mean.

```
> aggregate(x=CO2[,c("uptake")], by=data.frame(CO2$Plant),
  FUN="mean")
```

	CO2.Plant	x
1	Qn1	33.22857
2	Qn2	35.15714
3	Qn3	37.61429
4	Qc1	29.97143
5	Qc3	32.58571
6	Qc2	32.70000
7	Mn3	24.11429
8	Mn2	27.34286
9	Mn1	26.40000
10	Mc2	12.14286
11	Mc3	17.30000
12	Mc1	18.00000

We'll wrap up this discussion up with an example of how to do a **SQL JOIN** using R. Consider the case where you'd like to look up the country from a secondary table that maps states and provinces to countries. Here is the SQL statement to achieve this:

```
SELECT c.Type,
c.Plant,
c.Treatment,
c.conc,
c.uptake,
g.country
FROM geo_map g
LEFT JOIN CO2 c ON(c.Type = g.Type)
```

The R equivalent uses the following syntax based on the merge() function. Looking at the first few observations from the CO2 data set, we see the variable Type, which contains the state or province of origin for the plant. We'll use this variable as the common key value. Next, we'll create a new data frame, geo_map, which will play the role of a look-up table in which the country is paired with the state/province. Then, after assigning appropriate column names for geo_map, we will use merge() to produce the equivalent of a SQL joined result set, joinCO2. Notice that the new data frame contains a variable country, which is the look-up value based on Type. This has the same effect as the SQL JOIN.

```
> head(CO2)
    Plant  Type    Treatment   conc   uptake
1   Qn1    Quebec  nonchilled  95     16.0
2   Qn1    Quebec  nonchilled  175    30.4
3   Qn1    Quebec  nonchilled  250    34.8
4   Qn1    Quebec  nonchilled  350    37.2
5   Qn1    Quebec  nonchilled  500    35.3
6   Qn1    Quebec  nonchilled  675    39.2

> stateprov <- c("Mississippi", "California", "Victoria", "New South
    Wales", "Quebec", "Ontario")
> country <- c("United States", "United States", "Australia",
    "Australia", "Canada", "Canada")

> geo_map <- data.frame(country=country, stateprov=stateprov)
> geo_map
    country          Type  stateprov
1   United States    Mississippi
2   United States    California
3   Australia        Victoria
4   Australia        New South Wales
5   Canada           Quebec
6   Canada           Ontario
```

```
> colnames(geo_map) <- c("country", "Type")
> joinCO2 <- merge(CO2, geo_map, by=c("Type"))
> head(joinCO2)
  Type         Plant  Treatment   conc   uptake      country
1 Mississippi  Mn1    nonchilled  95     10.6        United States
2 Mississippi  Mn1    nonchilled  175    19.2        United States
3 Mississippi  Mn1    nonchilled  250    26.2        United States
4 Mississippi  Mn1    nonchilled  350    30.0        United States
5 Mississippi  Mn1    nonchilled  500    30.9        United States
6 Mississippi  Mn1    nonchilled  675    32.4        United States
```

READING TWITTER DATA

As data science continues to evolve at a rapid pace, we're seeing an increased interest in unstructured data sources from social media to add color to traditional data sources. Arguably the most popular social media data source is Twitter. The term "unstructured" is used to describe social media data because it does not fall into the usual tabular format that typical corporate transactional data does. Unstructured data are free form, just plain text, or, in the case of Tweets, 140 characters of words, abbreviations, handles, hashtags, and special symbols. The first step in utilizing this kind of data is to read it into the R environment just like any other data source. In this section, we'll step through the process of reading Tweets using R.

Unfortunately, the process of using Twitter as a data source is somewhat arduous due to the security requirements that are necessitated by Twitter as of March 2013 (it was a lot easier prior to that date!). You must have a Twitter account and provide authentication to this account from your R code.

To begin, we'll install the twitteR package that facilitates reading Tweets. It is an R-based Twitter client that provides an interface to the Twitter web API. This package also contains the ROAuth library (open authentication) that is necessary for us to authenticate ourselves with Twitter.

```
> install.packages("twitteR")   # Contains ROAuth
```

```
> library(twitteR)
> library(ROAuth)
```

Next, we'll define a few variables to hold special URLs for communicating with Twitter: `requestURL`, `accessURL`, and `authURL`. Also, if you are a Windows user, you'll need to download a special CA (community driven certificate authority) cert file from the URL provided below.

```
> requestURL <- "https://api.twitter.com/oauth/request_token"
> accessURL <- "https://api.twitter.com/oauth/access_token"
> authURL <- "https://api.twitter.com/oauth/authorize"
> download.file(url="http://curl.haxx.se/ca/cacert.pem",
    destfile="cacert.pem")
```

Next, you need to create a Twitter application by going to the URL http://dev.twitter.com/apps/new and logging in with your Twitter account. Then you'll enter details on the page in order to get the consumer key and consumer secret by using the Test Auth button. You need to copy/paste the keys into your R code:

```
> consumerKey <- "tu4dkb9fHLgLrNptaI2CA"
> consumerSecret <- "UzlhoMFyF9IZ6bxxG89DLdPB74VUzur3mBWcr6LcVE"
> Cred <- OAuthFactory$new(consumerKey=consumerKey,
            consumerSecret=consumerSecret,
            requestURL=requestURL,
            accessURL=accessURL,
            authURL=authURL)
```

Now enter the following line to ask Twitter to provide you with a numeric PIN number. You'll see a message in the R console directing you to copy/paste a special URL displayed in the console into your browser (NOTE: if you're unable to highlight the URL in the console to copy it to your clipboard, you need to upgrade your RStudio installation). Once you do that, the Twitter API will display a web page containing a PIN of 7 digits. You will need to type those digits into the console, which should be waiting for your input.

```
> Cred$handshake(cainfo = system.file("CurlSSL", "cacert.pem",
    package = "RCurl") )
```

At this point, you can save your Twitter authentication for later use using the `save()` function. Finally, you need to register your Twitter authentication with the `registerTwitterOAuth()` function from the `twitteR` package.

```
> save(Cred, file="twitter authentication.Rdata")
> registerTwitterOAuth(Cred)
[1] TRUE
```

If you wish to read Tweets in the future, all you need to do is use the following code:

```
> load("twitter authentication.Rdata")
> registerTwitterOAuth(Cred)
```

At long last, we're ready to read some Tweets. In the code that follows, we use the `searchTwitter()` function and pass it a search keyword; in this case, the hashtag #MLB for major league baseball. The Twitter API limits the number of Tweets you can read to 499. The Tweets are returned in a list, so we use the `twListToDF()` function to convert it to a data frame, which is more convenient when doing analysis. Lastly, we can write out the Tweets to a CSV file for safe keeping.

```
> MLB.list <- searchTwitter('#MLB', n=499, cainfo="cacert.pem")
> MLB.df = twListToDF(MLB.list)
> write.csv(MLB.df, file='MLBTweets.csv', row.names=F)
```

READING DATA FROM GOOGLE ANALYTICS

Another very useful source of data is Google Analytics. Many companies use this Google website statistics service to provide insight into how their site is being used. The level of sophistication of Google Analytics is amazing, and the best part about it is that the service is free of charge to use. Once integrated into a website (using a small Google-provided code snippet that you can add to your site), a large amount of data is collected for analysis purposes. Although Google offers an impressive set of tools for analyzing site statistics, you can access the data directly so that you can perform your own custom machine learning algorithms on the data. In this section, we'll see how to go about accessing Google Analytics data.

There are two ways to access Google Analytics data. First, you can login to Google Analytics using the account you've set up for the website you're tracking. Each report that you can run has an Export feature that can be used to download the raw data for the report. The idea would be to run a particular report with a wide date range so you'll get a good sample of data for machine learning analysis. We'll see an example of this in an example below. The other method for accessing Google Analytics data is to use the RGoogleAnalytics package, which contains a number of different R functions that allow you to use the Google Analytics Data Export API. We'll see an example of this method below as well.

Let's start with the export method of accessing Google Analytics data. For this example, I logged onto a Google Analytics account I use for monitoring a client's website. I selected one of the Standard Reports via: Traffic Sources -> Sources -> All Traffic. After viewing the report, from the top horizontal menu I selected: Export -> Excel (XLSX) and saved the file in the data folder of my working directory. The Excel file produced by Google Analytics has multiple sheets, usually one Summary sheet and one or more Datasheets. Based on what you intend to do with the data, you'll have to decide which sheet to read into R. Google Analytics uses some column names that are not compatible with the xlsx package, so you'll have to open the file in Excel to manually edit one or more potentially offending column names. For example, you'll need to change the column name Pages / Visit to something more R friendly like Pages_Visit. Figure 2-4 shows a sheet that is ready to read into R using:

```
> library(xlsx)
> GA <- read.xlsx2("./data/Analytics_All_Traffic.xlsx",
    sheetIndex=2)
> head(GA)
    Source_Medium Visits    Pages_Visit Avg_Visit_Duration
1       google / organic 1349.0 5.638991845811712
    151.54558932542625
2       (direct) / (none) 562.0 4.119217081850533 114.98220640569394
```

```
3 fashiondistrict.org / referral 242.0 3.9214876033057853
    140.30578512396696
4        yahoo / organic  73.0 3.6301369863013697 66.53424657534246
5         bing / organic  71.0 5.549295774647887 104.14084507042253
6     oohlaluxe.net / referral  36.0 4.361111111111111
    116.80555555555556
  Percent_New_Visits      Bounce_Rate
1  0.614529280948851      0.5181616011860638
2  0.597864768683274      0.5747330960854092
3  0.8099173553719008     0.45041322314049587
4  0.684931506849315      0.410958904109589
5  0.647887323943662      0.29577464788732394
6  0.8888888888888888     0.3611111111111111
```

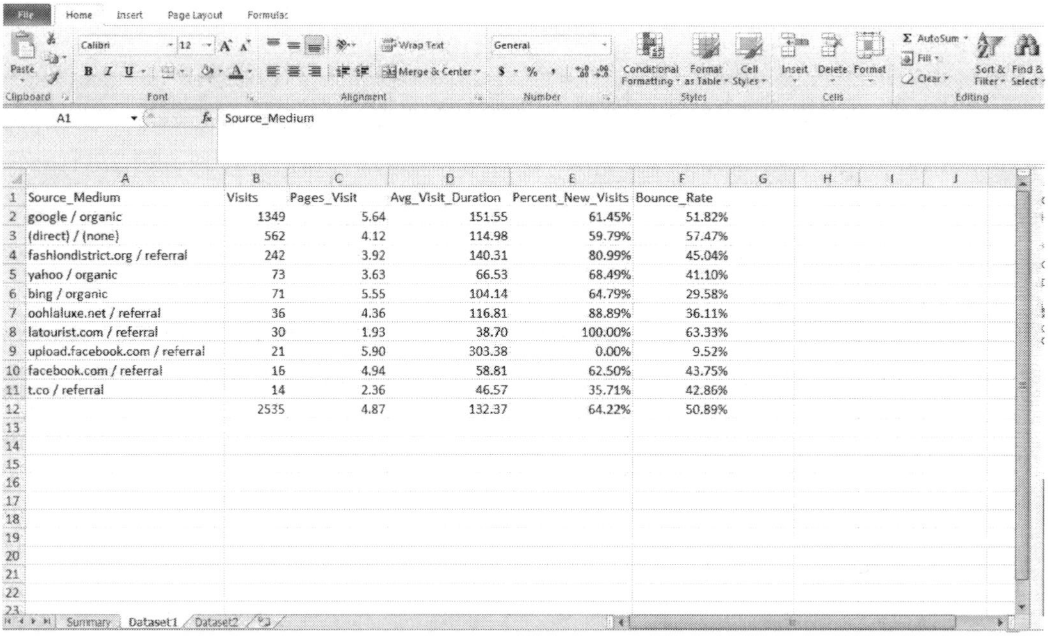

Source_Medium	Visits	Pages_Visit	Avg_Visit_Duration	Percent_New_Visits	Bounce_Rate
google / organic	1349	5.64	151.55	61.45%	51.82%
(direct) / (none)	562	4.12	114.98	59.79%	57.47%
fashiondistrict.org / referral	242	3.92	140.31	80.99%	45.04%
yahoo / organic	73	3.63	66.53	68.49%	41.10%
bing / organic	71	5.55	104.14	64.79%	29.58%
oohlaluxe.net / referral	36	4.36	116.81	88.89%	36.11%
latourist.com / referral	30	1.93	38.70	100.00%	63.33%
upload.facebook.com / referral	21	5.90	303.38	0.00%	9.52%
facebook.com / referral	16	4.94	58.81	62.50%	43.75%
t.co / referral	14	2.36	46.57	35.71%	42.86%
	2535	4.87	132.37	64.22%	50.89%

Figure 2-4 Google Analytics All Traffic Sources report

Now let's look at using the RGoogleAnalytics API using the `RGoogleAnalytics` package. From R, you'll need to authenticate yourself through the `OAuth2` routine, create a query, and then save the results in a data frame. Before you get started, the `RGoogleAnalytics` library has dependencies on two other libraries: RCurl, which provides https support from within R, and RJSON, which provides support for parsing the RJSON response from the API.

```
> install.packages("RCurl")
> install.packages("RJSON")
> library("RGoogleAnalytics")
```

The following statements open a browser window, allowing you to authenticate yourself with Google's OAuth2. Following the instructions on the page will allow you to copy the Access Token to your clipboard and then paste it in the R console, as directed.

```
> query <- QueryBuilder()
> access_token <- query$authorize()
```

Next, the following statements will create a new Google Analytics API object using the access_token you obtained above.

```
> ga <- RGoogleAnalytics()
> ga.profiles <- ga$GetProfileData(access_token)
> ga.profiles      # List the GA profiles
```

The following statement is the main part of the process of reading Google Analytics as a data source. You build the query string and use the profile by setting its index value.

```
> query$Init(start.date = "2013-07-01",
      end.date = "2013-07-01",
      dimensions - "ga:date,ga:pagePath",
      metrics = "ga:visits,ga:pageviews,ga:timeOnPage",
      sort = "ga:visits",
      #filters="",
      #segment="",
      max.results = 99,
      table.id =
        paste("ga:",ga.profiles$id[1],sep="",collapse=","),
```

```
        access_token=access_token)
```

```
> ga.data <- ga$GetReportData(query)
```

```
[1] "Your query matched 88 results that are stored to dataframe
    ga.data"
```

```
> head(ga.data)
```

```
#  date      pagePath
1  20130701 /SearchResult.asp?Type=ALL&String=&CompanyID=127&CategoryID=0
2  20130701 /SearchResult.asp?Type=ALL&String=&CompanyID=130&CategoryID=0
3  20130701 /SearchResult.asp?Type=ALL&String=&CompanyID=175&CategoryID=0
4  20130701 /SearchResult.asp?Type=ALL&String=&CompanyID=181&CategoryID=0
5  20130701 /SearchResult.asp?Type=ALL&String=&CompanyID=184&CategoryID=0
6  20130701 /SearchResult.asp?Type=ALL&String=&CompanyID=186&CategoryID=0
```

```
   visits   pageviews   timeOnPage
1  0        3           11
2  0        4           20
3  0        2           13
4  0        1           1
5  0        2           11
6  0        3           6
```

WRITING DATA

Although importing external files into R is generally what a data scientist does when working on a machine learning project, it is sometimes necessary to write data from the R environment to an external file. Fortunately, many of the data access R packages we've seen in this chapter also provide the ability to write files. For example, we have the `write.table()` function, which allows you to write a CSV file. In the example below, we will use R to remove the first column of the data frame (the `POST_ID` variable) and write out a new version of the CSV without this variable. Then, just to prove it worked, we read the new CSV file back in and use `head()` to show the first few rows.

```
> tempDF <- SFParkingMeters[,-1]   # Remove POST_ID variable
```

```
> write.table(tempDF, file="./data/newSFParkingMeters.csv", sep=",")
> newSFParkingMeters <- read.table("./data/newSFParkingMeters.csv",
    sep=",")
> head(newSFParkingMeters)
```

	MS_ID	MS_SPACEID	CAP_COLOR	METER_TYPE	SMART_METE	ACTIVESENS	JURISDICTI	ON_OFF_STR
1	–	0	Grey	SS	Y	Y	SFMTA	ON
2	–	0	Green	SS	Y	Y	SFMTA	ON
3	–	0	Yellow	SS	Y	Y	SFMTA	ON
4	–	0	Grey	SS	N	N	SFMTA	ON
5	–	0	Grey	SS	N	N	SFMTA	ON
6	–	0	Grey	SS	Y	Y	SFMTA	ON

	OSP_ID	STREET_NUM	STREETNAME	STREET_SEG	RATEAREA	SFPARKAREA
1	0	2016	CHESTNUT ST	3977000	Area 5	Marina
2	0	2103	CHESTNUT ST	3979000	Area 5	Marina
3	0	2116	CHESTNUT ST	3979000	Area 5	Marina
4	0	525	COLUMBUS AVE	4295000	Area 3	
5	0	527	COLUMBUS AVE	4295000	Area 3	
6	0	412	HAYES ST	6816000	Area 5	Civic Center

	LOCATION
1	(37.800798, -122.43687)
2	(37.800522, -122.438067)
3	(37.800589, -122.438525)
4	(37.800053, -122.409985)
5	(37.800088, -122.410035)
6	(37.776878, -122.423512)

In a similar vein, the xlsx package has the write.xlsx() function, the rjson package has the toJSON() function, etc.

SUMMARY

In this chapter, we learned how data sources are the lifeblood of the machine learning equation. We've seen a number of ways to access raw data and get it into the R environment for the purpose of using it with machine learning algorithms. The next step will be to take the raw data and "process" it for consumption by your selected algorithm. This is called "data munging," and is the topic for Chapter 3.

Here is a summary of what you've learned in this chapter:

- Data for machine learning comes in all shapes and sizes including CSV, Excel, and JSON, just to name a few.
- Using various R packages, you can directly access data residing in SQL database tables.
- Unstructured data from social media sources like Twitter have become popular data sources for machine learning applications. With R, you can easily access Twitter as a data source.
- Google Analytics represents another exciting source of data for machine learning.
- You can easily write data from R to an external file.

Chapter 3
Data Munging

"Data munging" is an unusual term used to describe the part of a data science project involving the transformation of a data set into a form more suitable for machine learning algorithms. Data munging constitutes one of the primary ingredients of the "data pipeline," the series of processing steps required to take raw data and transform it for use in a production system. The task involves cleansing, converting, manipulating, parsing, filtering, and mapping data in a "raw" form into a more refined form. Data munging is a very important step in the machine learning process that often takes up to 80% of the time and cost involved in the overall project. Think of data munging as an important data pre-processing step to prepare the data for machine learning algorithms. Data munging can be tedious, but the goals and benefits are proven; data processed through data munging makes data analysis and machine learning much easier (or at least possible). In addition, the munging process makes the data easy to model and visualize.

One of the main goals of data munging is to tidy up the data; i.e., each variable forms a column, each observation forms a row, and each table stores data about one kind of observation. The data you obtain from domain experts does not always fit into the model of data compatible with machine learning (in fact, it rarely does), so your job is to plan a series of steps in a workflow, starting with the raw data and ending in the training data for a machine learning algorithm. It is very important to document all the steps you take in data munging in order to have a reproducible analysis process. You should keep all the R scripts you use for data munging and note the order in which you ran them.

As you examine your raw data set, here are some best practice guidelines you might consider in deciding which data munging tasks are necessary for your particular project:

- Column names should be easy to use and informative

- Row names should be easy to use and informative

- Obvious errors in the data should be repaired if possible or removed

- Values of variables should be in a consistent format (e.g., dates in YYYYMMDD)

- Values of variables should be consistent (e.g., a country variable should only have one representation: US, USA, or United States)

- Minimal missing values

- Appropriate transformed variables have been added

In order to achieve the above items, a number of data munging operations must be performed on the data. The specific operations you'll need to perform depend on your specific data as well as on the requirements underlying your machine learning problem. Your starting point is important. If you start with something like what's shown in Figure 3-1, a lot of work is in store for you.

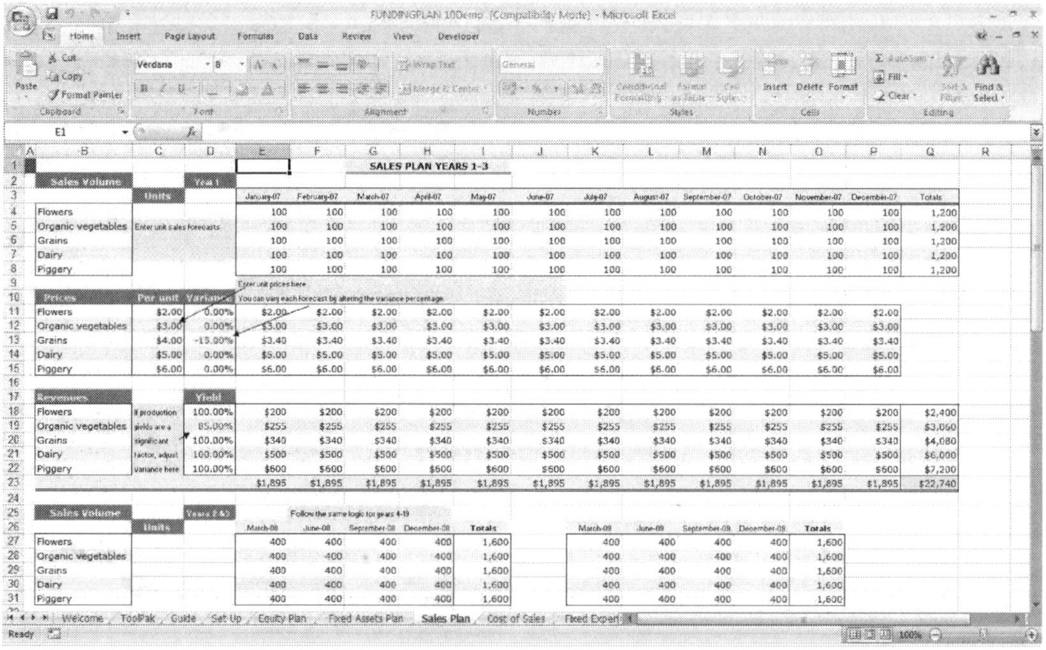

Figure 3-1 A typical Excel management report not conducive to importing into R

Although the data looks orderly, the spreadsheet has several categories of data with different structures/layouts (e.g., the number of columns for each segment is different). You cannot easily import this kind of data into R, so some rearrangement in Excel is required before you read it into R. On the other hand, you'd be fortunate to start with what's shown in Figure 3-2. All of the observations (rows) are nicely arranged, and the feature variables (columns) are in a consistent format with no missing values. If Excel is the container of the raw data you're given for the data science project, it will behoove you to quickly manipulate the rows and columns before you import it into R. As just one example, if the data in Excel is organized by rows but you prefer columns, then Excel has an easy-to-use *Transpose* tool that you can use to perform this operation.

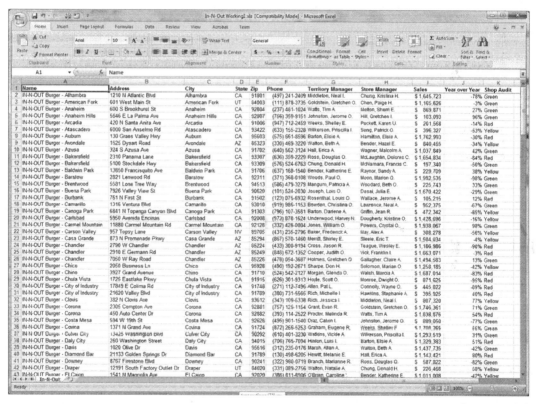

Figure 3-2 Example of an orderly starting point for data munging

What we'll attempt to do in this chapter is to present a "data munging toolbox" that you can draw from to suit your needs as you work on machine learning projects. You may end up needing only a fraction of the tools we present here.

On the other hand, you may need additional transformative tools, in which case you'll have to devise your own methods using the tools presented here as the foundation for new tools you might need. Over time, you're likely to develop a large library of data munging tools that you can choose from when the need arises. Here is a list of some commonly used operations that we'll cover in this chapter:

- Data sampling
- Revise variable names
- Create new variables
- Discretize numeric values
- Date handling
- Binary categorical variables
- Merge data sets
- Order data sets
- Reshape data sets
- Data manipulation using `dplyr`
- Handle missing data
- Feature scaling
- Dimensionality reduction

Fortunately, R has a long list of both built-in tools and tools from a number of R packages to fully address the needs of data munging. Just a few packages that will come in handy are `plyr`, `dplyr`, `reshape2`, `stringr`, and `lubridate`. We'll see examples of these packages in the sections that follow.

FEATURE ENGINEERING

Feature engineering is the identification of the subset of data or transformed data that you want to use in your model or machine learning algorithm. Different branches of academia use different terms to describe the same thing. Statisticians use "explanatory variables," "dependent variables," or "predictors" when describing the subset of data that is used as input to a model. Data scientists, on the other hand, use "features." It is quite possible that you have many redundancies or correlated variables in your raw data set, and you don't want to include all those variables in your model. Similarly, you may wish to create new variables by transforming existing variables in some way, e.g., turning a continuous variable into a binary variable, before handing them off to the model.

Feature engineering is the most important but underrated step of machine learning. It is an important part of building statistical models and algorithms, in general. Just because you have data doesn't mean all of it has to be used in the model. It is often said that better, more well-conceived features are more valuable than algorithms. Since the data munging task involves working with raw data and it takes place in the early stage of the machine learning process, it is a prime time to have an eye for feature engineering.

Good feature engineering involves two processes. First, you must understand the properties of the problem you're trying to solve and how they might interact with the strengths and limitations of the algorithm you're using. Second, experimental work in which you test your expectations and find out what actually works and what doesn't needs to be performed. These can be done iteratively; your *top down* understanding of the problem motivates experiments, and then the *bottom up* information you learn from those experiments helps you obtain a better understanding of the problem. The deeper understanding of the problem can then drive more experiments. Often, feature engineering is a give-and-take process with exploratory data analysis, which we'll see in Chapter 4. Feature engineering is when you use your knowledge about the data to select and create features that make machine learning algorithms work better.

The process of feature engineering is as much of an art as a science. It's good to have a domain expert around for this process, but it's also good to use your imagination. The problem is often too much data. With today's big data technology, we're in a position to generate a large number of features. This wasn't always the case. Just a few years ago, a typical survey might yield responses to 20 questions rather than the hundreds of data items possible today. The question you need to answer is how many of these features are just noise? In the environment of big data, some of the information you can capture might not be useful.

Although feature engineering is an ongoing topic of research, let's review a simple approach that you can combine with the data munging task and also couple with the supervised learning topics to come in later chapters. Let's say you come up with a group of features after completing the data munging process. You can start with a regression model with no features and then gradually add one feature at a time according to which feature improves the model the most. You basically build all possible regression models with a single predictor and then you pick the best. Now try all possible models that include that best predictor plus a second predictor. Pick the best of those. You keep adding one feature at a time, and you stop when your model no longer improves but instead gets worse.

Another approach involves backward elimination of features. Here, you start with a regression model that includes all of the features, and you gradually remove one feature at a time according to the feature whose removal makes the biggest improvement. You stop removing features when removing the feature makes the predictive model get worse.

Just as a reminder before we move on, if you have access to a domain expert, tap into their expertise of the business and knowledge of the data before you engage in a lengthy feature engineering process.

DATA PIPELINE

With machine learning projects, it is very important to keep your data munging code organized and well commented. The reason is that you will invariably need to go back and review all of the individual steps you went through to arrive at the final form of the data set used by the machine learning algorithm. I suggest that you keep all your code snippets in a central R script file or working directory. The script(s) will become the basis of your *data pipeline*. A data pipeline is a deterministic series of data transformation tasks that are required to take a raw data set and turn it into a transformed data set ready for machine learning. You will typically need to re-run your data pipeline over and over again to refresh your machine learning data sets with more current data. One of the characteristics of machine learning, as we'll see in later chapters, is the need to retrain the algorithms with more current data in order to improve their predictive power.

In the sections that follow, I'll present a data munging toolkit of techniques to use on your data. The order of these discussions is roughly the order in which they should be applied, but not necessarily so. The exact order depends heavily on the data set being pre-processed and the needs of the machine learning algorithm being used. The specific data munging steps you choose will represent the early stages of your machine learning data pipeline.

DATA SAMPLING

In some cases, the amount of data you're given for a machine learning problem is large, and attempting to process it within the R environment can be problematic since R is memory based and the processing power at your disposal may be limited. In these cases, it may be appropriate to sample the data set to reduce the size of the data to be processed.

There are many sampling models, but random sampling is by far the most common model—assigning a uniform probability to each record for "being chosen." Sampling can be done without replacement (each record can be picked at most once) or with replacement (same record can be picked more than once). Let's use the iris data set for an example of sampling. We can use the sample() function to randomly select ten rows with replacement. The resulting sample_index is an integer vector containing an index to the iris data set records selected. We use this sample index to create a new sample data set, samplet_set, as shown below.

```
> sample_index <-sample(1:nrow(iris), 10, replace=T)          1:10
> sample_index
 [1] 25 134 116 140 91 98 18 49 17 73     ← index, i.e. row #s of rows
> sample_set <- iris[sample_index,]                 sampled
> sample_set                                      ← subset
```

	Sepal.Length	Sepal.Width	Petal.Length	Petal.Width	Species
25	4.8	3.4	1.9	0.2	setosa
134	6.3	2.8	5.1	1.5	virginica
116	6.4	3.2	5.3	2.3	virginica
140	6.9	3.1	5.4	2.1	virginica

91	5.5	2.6	4.4	1.2	versicolor
98	6.2	2.9	4.3	1.3	versicolor
18	5.1	3.5	1.4	0.3	setosa
49	5.3	3.7	1.5	0.2	setosa
17	5.4	3.9	1.3	0.4	setosa
73	6.3	2.5	4.9	1.5	versicolor

REVISE VARIABLE NAMES

Receiving data sets from different sources around an organization, you'll often find inconsistent, inconvenient, and sometimes improper field naming conventions used for the feature variables included in the file. Many times, unusual variable names come from old legacy systems that are incompatible with modern software technology. It is your job as a data scientist to improve usability, and this requires renaming and reforming the names. Here are some potential problems you might encounter with variable naming, but there could be many other issues; you just have to write code to enforce naming conventions that are right for you:

- employeeSalary: Mixed case name, some practitioners believe it is best to have all lower case.

- office.1: Special characters embedded in name such as the period "." are used frequently in the R community. You may choose to eliminate all special characters.

- Country of Origin: Blank spaces in the name are not supported in R, so all embedded spaces must be removed.

- zip_code: Use of underscore characters is common in other programming languages, and some R practitioners use them, too.

Now let's take a look at an example of how we might correct some variable naming problems using R programming. First, we'll create a null data frame, i.e., a data frame with column names but no actual data. For some R practitioners, some of the column names in the example will need correcting, e.g., `CrossStreet` is converted to `crossstreet` using the `tolower()` function.

```
> df <- data.frame("Address 1"=character(0), direction=character(0),
    street=character(0), CrossStreet=character(0),
    intersection=character(0), Location.1=character(0))
> names(df)
[1]"Address.1" "direction" "street" "CrossStreet" "intersection"
[6]"Location.1"
> names(df) <- tolower(names(df))   # convert to all lower case
> names(df)
[1]"address.1" "direction" "street" "crossstreet" "intersection"
[6]"location.1"
```

creates null df columns names but no data (handwritten annotation)

In the next code segment, we'll use the `strsplit()` function to go through all the variable names and split up any name that contains an embedded period. The output of `strsplit()` is an R list object. The way this base R function works is when it finds a string with a period, it splits it into a sub-list where the first element of the sub-list contains the part of the string before the period and the second element of the sub-list has the part after the period.

```
> splitnames <- strsplit(names(df), "\\.")
> class(splitnames)
[1] "list"
> length(splitnames)
[1] 6
> splitnames[2]     # Single list element
[[1]]
[1] "direction"
> splitnames[6]     # Sub-list element
[[1]]
[1] "location" "1"
> splitnames[[6]][1]  # "location"
[1] "location"
> splitnames[[6]][2]  # "1"
```

```
[1] "1"
```

In the last part of this example, we will write a special R function, `firstelement()`, that goes through the entire `splitnames` list object and selects only the first part of each sub-list (remember, our test data frame has two variable names containing a period character "."), then properly sets the variable names. Note that `firstelement()` is called repeatedly, once for each element in `splitnames` to pull out the first element of the sub-list.

```
> firstelement <- function(x){x[1]}
names(df) <- sapply(splitnames, firstelement)
```

CREATE NEW VARIABLES

similar to next section

During the data munging process, you may review the existing features in the data set and determine that you need a new variable, possibly a calculated variable derived from the existing variables. R makes it easy to add new variables to an existing data frame. To illustrate this concept, we'll use the `airquality` data set and add a new field, `ozoneRanges`. This field will take the current quantitative variable `Ozone` and calculate a corresponding range based on its value. To do this, we'll use the `cut()` function, which allows us to categorize each `Ozone` value according to the range in which it falls. For example, the `Ozone` value 41 falls within the range (25, 50].

```
> airquality$Ozone[1:10]  # First 10 rows of Ozone values
[1] 41 36 12 18 NA 28 23 19 8 NA
> ozoneRanges <- cut(airquality$Ozone, seq(0,200,by=25))
> ozoneRanges[1:10] # Show calculated ranges of Ozone values
[1] (25,50] (25,50] (0,25] (0,25] <NA>  (25,50] (0,25] (0,25] (0,25]
[10] <NA>
8 Levels: (0,25] (25,50] (50,75] (75,100] (100,125] (125,150] ...
    (175,200]
> class(ozoneRanges) # Note, this is a factor!
[1] "factor"
> table(ozoneRanges, useNA="ifany")
```

```
ozoneRanges
 (0,25]   (25,50]   (50,75]  (75,100]  (100,125]  (125,150]  (150,175]
  50        32        12        15         5          1          1
(175,200]    <NA>
  0          37
> airquality$ozoneRanges <- ozoneRanges
> head(airquality)
    Ozone   Solar.R   Wind   Temp   Month   Day   ozoneRanges
1    41      190      7.4     67      5       1     (25,50]
2    36      118      8.0     72      5       2     (25,50]
3    12      149      12.6    74      5       3     (0,25]
4    18      313      11.5    62      5       4     (0,25]
5    NA      NA       14.3    56      5       5     <NA>
6    28      NA       14.9    66      5       6     (25,50]
```

paste into df (handwritten annotation)

Other examples of adding new, derived features would be to calculate a ratio of two variables or to generalize some features to a coarser grain such as converting a geographical location to a zip code or converting an age variable to an age group.

DISCRETIZE NUMERIC VALUES

On occasion, you'll be presented with a numeric variable in a data set that would be more convenient for machine learning if the continuous values were represented as discrete "ranges" of values instead. For example, you might have a field called salary, but instead of the actual salary amount, a series of six value ranges would be more useful—say $0 - $10,000, $10,001 - $25,000, $25,001 - $50,000, $50,001 - $75,000, $75,001 - $100,000, and $100,001 - $150,000. So if a particular record had a salary value of $56,000, then the discrete version would be the range $50,001 - $75,000. Dividing a continuous value variable into ranges, creating a new factor variable for the range value, and assigning the value of the corresponding bucket of the range in which it falls is called "discretizing." We can easily perform this operation using the cut() function in R.

In the example below, we work to discretize the iris data set's Sepal.Length variable. We arbitrarily decided to cut the values into ten buckets. To do this, we use the seq() function to create the appropriate number of cut points based on the maximum and minimum values found for this variable and the number of buckets chosen. Then we use the cut() function to create a factor object containing the range buckets corresponding to each Sepal.Length value. Finally, to illustrate the point, the factor is combined with the original Sepal.Length values in a new data frame newiris.

```
> data(iris)
> buckets <- 10
> maxSepLen <- max(iris$Sepal.Length)        Find max value
> minSepLen <- min(iris$Sepal.Length)          "    min    "
> cutPoints <- seq(minSepLen, maxSepLen, by=(maxSepLen-
    minSepLen)/buckets)
[1] 4.30 4.66 5.02 5.38 5.74 6.10 6.46 6.82 7.18 7.54 7.90
> cutSepLen <-
    cut(iris$Sepal.Length,breaks=cutPoints,include.lowest=TRUE)
> newiris <- data.frame(contSepLen=iris$Sepal.Length,    new df
    discSepLen=cutSepLen)
> head(newiris)   # Display first 6 records of data frame
    contSepLen     discSepLen
1     5.1         (5.02,5.38]
2     4.9         (4.66,5.02]
3     4.7         (4.66,5.02]
4     4.6         [4.3,4.66]
5     5.0         (4.66,5.02]
6     5.4         (5.38,5.74]
```

DATE HANDLING

Date values present a particularly thorny issue when performing data munging tasks in R. The reason is partly because there are so many representations of date and time values in data sets and also because the R syntax for dealing with dates can be inconvenient and confusing. This subject could fill an entire chapter, so in this section we'll only cover a few common situations and corresponding solutions. This is one area in data munging where practice makes perfect, so after finishing this book, you should explore several data sets from your area of domain interest and develop procedures for handling the date and time data values that you encounter.

Dates come in many different formats, which makes recognizing and parsing them a challenge. When performing data munging, you must be aware of the format used for date values in the data set. You also must have an idea of how you'd like the dates to appear once you get the data into R. For example, do you need a full date (MM/DD/YYYY) or just the month and year (MMYYYY)?

The base R mechanisms for data handling can be difficult to use, but luckily, there is a very handy package called lubridate that makes handling dates much easier. I strongly recommend that you become familiar with this package for your data munging tasks. In this section, we'll only consider using lubridate. The lubridate package contains a data set called lakers that we'll use for examples. The data set contains play by play statistics for each basketball game played by the Los Angeles Lakers in the 2008-2009 season. The data set contains two fields of interest: lakers$date (an integer value for the date of the game) and lakers$time (a character value for the time on the game clock when the play was made).

In the code below, we'll load the lubridate package and the lakers data set. Since we plan to do some data munging on the date and time variables, let's make a copy of the data frame and call it df. Using str(df$date) tells us that the class of this variable is integer and the format of the data is year, month, and day. This kind of thing is typical, where date and time values are not stored as actual R date or time objects, but rather as integer or character. It is our job to convert the values accordingly.

```
> library(lubridate)
> data(lakers)
> df <- lakers   # Make a copy for testing
> str(df$date)
```

```
int [1:34624] 20081028 20081028 20081028 20081028 20081028 20081028
    20081028 20081028 20081028 20081028 ...
```

What we'd like to do as part of our data munging is to combine the `date` and `time` variables into a single R date object that includes the time. You may wish to do this, for example, so you can compute the elapsed time from one play to another. As with other data munging tasks, we can start by experimenting with a single observation and store the variable values in `playdate` and `playtime`. Then we `paste()` them together, creating `playdatetime`. Note that in the `paste()` function, the integer value for `playdate` is cast (converted to another class) to character and then combined with `playtime`. Finally, we use `parse_date_time()` from the `lubridate` package to produce an R date object. We also display the new combined date/time value and its class. `POSIXct` is the R class representing calendar dates and times.

```
> playdate <- df$date[1]   # Integer
> playtime <- df$time[1]   # Character
> playdatetime <- paste(playdate, playtime)
> playdatetime <- parse_date_time(playdatetime, "%y-%m-%d %H.%M")
> playdatetime
[1] "2008-10-28 12:00:00 UTC"
> class(playdatetime)
[1] "POSIXct" "POSIXt"
```

Another operation we can perform is to replace the integer form of the date variable value with its R date/time object equivalent. To do this, we can use `ymd()` from the lubridate package. Note that lubridate offers other functions, such as `mdy()` and `dmy()`, to match the format of the date values you find in your data set.

```
> df$date <- ymd(df$date)
> str(df$date)
POSIXct[1:34624], format: "2008-10-28" "2008-10-28" "2008-10-28"
    "2008-10-28" "2008-10-28" ...
> class(df$date)
[1] "POSIXct" "POSIXt"
```

Another thing we can do is create a new column, PlayDateTime, in the data frame. In order to achieve this, we can use the same parse_date_time() function, but this time for all observations in the data set.

```
> df$PlayDateTime <- parse_date_time(paste(df$date, df$time), "%y-
    %m-%d %H.%M")
> str(df$PlayDateTime)
POSIXct[1:34624], format: "2008-10-28 12:00:00" "2008-10-28
    11:39:00" "2008-10-28 11:37:00" ...
```

The above examples barely scratch the surface of date/time value data munging. Some other kinds of tasks you might need to perform are extracting components of dates/times such as years, months, seconds; switching between time zones; comparing times from places that use daylight savings time with times from places that do not; performing date and time arithmetic; handling leap years; etc. Typically, the goal is to parse (recognize) date and time values that are in non-standard or inconvenient formats and convert them into R date/time objects.

BINARY CATEGORICAL VARIABLES

When using certain machine learning algorithms, it is more convenient to have a categorical variable (called factors in R) represented as multiple binary variables. You might want to do this for use with a binary classifier algorithm. A good example of this can be seen with the iris data set's Species variable. This factor variable has three "levels": setosa, versicolor, and virginica. We'd like to create three new binary variables, each representing a TRUE or FALSE condition for the Species variable value of the record.

```
> species_cat <- levels(iris$Species)
> species_cat
[1] "setosa"    "versicolor" "virginica"
```

To achieve the desired results, we need to write a new function, binarySpecies(), that will be called repeatedly by the base R sapply() function in order to create a matrix containing the binary values representing Species. Next, we name the new columns according to the species name.

Finally, we attach the new columns to a copy of the iris data frame called bin_iris. We can now use this data frame with an appropriate machine learning algorithm.

```
> binarySpecies <- function(c) {return(iris$Species == c)}
```
new function

```
> newVars <- sapply(species_cat, binarySpecies)
> newVars[50:55,]
```
— why 50:55 ? arbitrary check?

	setosa	versicolor	virginica
[1,]	TRUE	FALSE	FALSE
[2,]	FALSE	TRUE	FALSE
[3,]	FALSE	TRUE	FALSE
[4,]	FALSE	TRUE	FALSE
[5,]	FALSE	TRUE	FALSE
[6,]	FALSE	TRUE	FALSE

```
> colnames(newVars) <- species_cat
> bin_matrix <- cbind(iris[,c('Species')], newVars)
```
this is done simply to coerce newVars logicals → integers

```
> bin_matrix[50:55,]
```

	setosa	versicolor	virginica
[1,]	1	1	0	0
[2,]	2	0	1	0
[3,]	2	0	1	0
[4,]	2	0	1	0
[5,]	2	0	1	0
[6,]	2	0	1	0

```
> bin_iris <- iris
> bin_iris$setosa <- bin_matrix[,2]
> bin_iris$versicolor <- bin_matrix[,3]
> bin_iris$virginica <- bin_matrix[,4]
> names(bin_iris)
[1] "Sepal.Length" "Sepal.Width" "Petal.Length" "Petal.Width"
    "Species"
[6] "setosa"      "versicolor"  "virginica"
```

MERGE DATA SETS

When you receive two or more data sets of similar structure, you may need to combine them to obtain the data set you'll use for machine learning purposes. The data munging phase is a good time to merge the data sets to form a new data set containing records from the contributing pieces. R has the very useful `merge()` function for merging data frames based on a common variable. If you're familiar with SQL, you may have guessed that `merge()` is very similar to a join operation. This is indeed the case, and the different arguments for `merge()` allow you to perform inner and outer joins, as well as left and right joins.

The `merge()` function allows four ways of combining data:

- **Inner join:** To keep only rows that match from the two data frames, specify the argument `all=FALSE`.

- **Outer join:** To keep all rows from both data frames, specify `all=TRUE`.

- **Left outer join:** To include all the rows of your data frame x and only those from y that match, specify `all.x=TRUE`.

- **Right outer join:** To include only those from x that match and all the rows of your data frame y, specify `all.y=TRUE`.

In the example below, we'll examine all four types of joins using `merge()` on a very simple set of data frames.

```
> df1 =
    data.frame(CustId=c(1:6),Product=c(rep("Mouse",3),rep("Keyboard"
    ,3)))
> df2 =
    data.frame(CustId=c(2,4,6),State=c(rep("California",2),rep("Oreg
    on",1)))
> # Outer join
> merge(x = df1, y = df2, by = "CustId", all - TRUE)
    CustId    Product          State
1   1         Mouse            <NA>
```

```
2    2              Mouse          California
3    3              Mouse          <NA>
4    4              Keyboard       California
5    5              Keyboard       <NA>
6    6              Keyboard       Oregon
> # Left outer join
> merge(x = df1, y = df2, by = "CustId", all.x=TRUE)
     CustId     Product        State
1    1              Mouse          <NA>
2    2              Mouse          California
3    3              Mouse          <NA>
4    4              Keyboard       California
5    5              Keyboard       <NA>
6    6              Keyboard       Oregon
> # Right outer join
> merge(x = df1, y = df2, by = "CustId", all.y=TRUE)
     CustId     Product        State
1    2              Mouse          California
2    4              Keyboard       California
3    6              Keyboard       Oregon
> # Inner join
> merge(x = df1, y = df2, by = "CustId", all=FALSE)
     CustId     Product        State
1    2              Mouse          California
2    4              Keyboard       California
3    6              Keyboard       Oregon
```

ORDERING DATA SETS

As you're evaluating your data sets for a new data science project, you'll often notice an ordering of the data that is natural to the problem being solved with machine learning. Maybe you're looking at real estate data of housing prices around the country. In this case, a geographical ordering by state, county and city might be appropriate for browsing through the data records instead of a random order, possibly the order that the records were originally added to the data set. To order the contents of the data frame to make it easier to browse, R has the order() function, which allows you to order a data frame by one or more variables.

Let's look at an example of ordering using the ToothGrowth data set. The first few records look like this:

```
> data(ToothGrowth)
> head(TooghGrowth)
    len   supp   dose
1   4.2   VC     0.5
2   11.5  VC     0.5
3   7.3   VC     0.5
4   5.8   VC     0.5
5   6.4   VC     0.5
6   10.0  VC     0.5
```

This data set consists of 60 observations with three numeric variables: len, supp, and dose. You can use ToothGrowth to learn more about this data set. We can use len to order the data set with the following R statement. We then display the first ten records of the resulting sorted data frame; notice the len column is now ordered.

```
> sortedData <- ToothGrowth[order(ToothGrowth$len),]
> sortedData[1:10,]
     len   supp   dose
1    4.2   VC     0.5
9    5.2   VC     0.5
4    5.8   VC     0.5
5    6.4   VC     0.5
10   7.0   VC     0.5
3    7.3   VC     0.5
37   8.2   OJ     0.5
38   9.4   OJ     0.5
```

```
34   9.7   OJ      0.5
40   9.7   OJ      0.5
```

In the next example, we'll order the `ToothGrowth` data set by two variables: `supp` and `len`. You can think of `supp` as the primary sort key and `len` as the secondary sort key. Here are the first ten records of the resorted data frame.

```
> sortedData <- ToothGrowth[order(ToothGrowth$supp,
      ToothGrowth$len),]
> sortedData[1:10,]
     len    supp   dose
37   8.2    OJ     0.5
38   9.4    OJ     0.5
34   9.7    OJ     0.5
40   9.7    OJ     0.5
36   10.0   OJ     0.5
35   14.5   OJ     0.5
49   14.5   OJ     1.0
31   15.2   OJ     0.5
39   16.5   OJ     0.5
33   17.6   OJ     0.5
```

RESHAPE DATA SETS

Many times you'll receive a data set that is "misshapen" for use with a machine learning algorithm, i.e., the data is all there, but it is in an inconvenient format or structure. When this happens, it is your job to reshape the data set to make it easier to perform downstream modeling. For these instances, you can use the `melt()` function found in the `reshape2` package. This function is a general purpose tool used to restructure a data set, but there are many possible examples of such data sets. We'll illustrate the process using just one such example.

We'll create a test data frame that we'll presume we received from an external source. The data set will contain the scores for two quizzes taken by three students in a class. The problem with the data set is that it has both scores for each student in the same row. For machine learning, it is more convenient to have a single score per row (we'll have twice as many rows).

```
> library(reshape2)
> misShaped <- as.data.frame(matrix(c(NA,5,1,4,2,3), byrow=TRUE,
    nrow=3))
> names(misShaped) <- c("Quiz 1", "Quiz 2")
> misShaped$student <- c("Ellen", "Catherine", "Stephen")
> misShaped
```

```
    Quiz 1  Quiz 2  student
1   NA      5       Ellen
2   1       4       Catherine
3   2       3       Stephen
```

In order to cure this structure problem, we'll reshape the data set using the melt() function. Here, we pass the data frame misShaped to the function and the name of the variable used to store values (in this case, score). The output of melt(), as you can see below, is exactly the structure we need.

```
> melt(misShaped, id.vars="student", variable.name="Quiz",
    value.name="score")
    student     Quiz     score
1   Ellen       Quiz 1   NA
2   Catherine   Quiz 1   1
3   Stephen     Quiz 1   2
4   Ellen       Quiz 2   5
5   Catherine   Quiz 2   4
6   Stephen     Quiz 2   3
```

DATA MANIPULATION USING DPLYR

The dplyr package is a valuable tool for the data munging process, providing the means to filter, select, restructure, and aggregate tabular data in R. dplyr is an improved version of the widely used plyr package, both created by noted R developer Hadley Wickham. Among key improvements, dplyr works exclusively with data frames; introduces a "grammar of data manipulation," allowing you to string together operations with the %.% operator; and is much faster than plyr or standard R operations. In this section, we'll see some examples of how dplyr assists with the data munging process. Note that dplyr offers alternate ways of doing data manipulation compared to techniques previously described in this chapter and Chapter 2: creating new variables, ordering data sets, SQL and SQL equivalents in R. Since dplyr is a single package with consistent syntax, you may choose to explore dplyr for many of your data munging tasks.

In this section, we'll illustrate the basic dplyr data manipulation verbs that work in a single table: filter(), arrange(), select(), and mutate(). There are other capabilities in dplyr, which you are encouraged to explore for your data munging work. We'll start by installing the dplyr package and loading the library and data set. We'll also use the tbl_df() function from dplyr, which optimizes a data frame for printing (minimizes output).

```
> install.packages("dplyr")
> library(dplyr)
> data(ToothGrowth)
> ToothGrowth_df <- tbl_df(ToothGrowth) # dplyr function
```

Next, we'll give an example of the filter() function, which is used to return a subset of the rows from the data set. In this case, we're creating a subset consisting of rows where the value of len is 11.2 and the value of supp is "VC." You might want to use this tool for selecting specific groups of data. In some ways, filter() is similar in function to a SQL SELECT statement, and its parameters are similar to a SQL WHERE clause.

```
> filter(ToothGrowth_df, len==11.2 & supp=="VC")
    len   supp   dose
1   11.2  VC     0.5
2   11.2  VC     0.5
```

Now we'll see an example of the arrange() function, which is used to reorder rows in a data set. In this case, we're reordering the ToothGrowth_df data frame to where the first sort sequence is by supp and the secondary sort is by len descending. This order is exhibited in the data displayed below. You might wish to reorder rows in a data set during exploratory data analysis, where you become familiar with the data. Ordering rows can help you determine the number of unique values for a particular variable, the range of values for a variable, the relative number of values for a variable, etc. You'll find that arrange() is similar in function to the order() function in base R that was described earlier in this chapter.

```
> arrange(ToothGrowth_df, supp, desc(len))
Source: local data frame [60 x 3]
```

	len	supp	dose
1	30.9	OJ	2.0
2	29.4	OJ	2.0
3	27.3	OJ	1.0
4	27.3	OJ	2.0
5	26.4	OJ	1.0
6	26.4	OJ	2.0
7	26.4	OJ	2.0
8	25.8	OJ	1.0
9	25.5	OJ	2.0
10	25.2	OJ	1.0

Let's turn to an example of the select() function, which returns only a subset of the columns in a data set. In this example, we eliminate the len variable and return a subset containing only dose and supp. Normally, you'd assign the return value of select() to another data frame. You may wish to use select() during a feature engineering exercise when you find some variables you'd like to eliminate from the data set. You'll find select() similar in function to a SQL SELECT statement that has an abbreviated field list, instead of all fields, as denoted with an asterisk.

```
> select(ToothGrowth_df, dose, supp)
```

```
Source: local data frame [60 x 2]
    dose supp
1   0.5   VC
2   0.5   VC
3   0.5   VC
4   0.5   VC
5   0.5   VC
6   0.5   VC
7   0.5   VC
8   0.5   VC
9   0.5   VC
10  0.5   VC
```

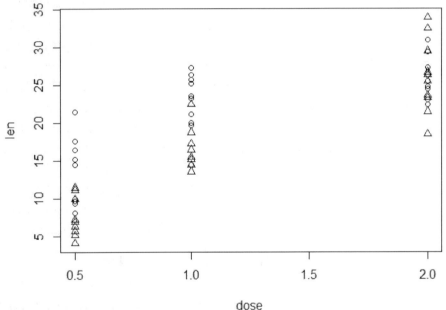

Figure 3-3 Plot of Tooth Growth data set using new variable supp_num

Finally, we can use the mutate() function to create a new column in the data set. In the example below, we create a new column, supp_num, which is the numeric equivalent of supp. We take the output of mutate() that contains the new column and assign it back to ToothGrowth_df. One final step is to use the new column in a `plot()` function to visualize the data set as shown in Figure 3-3. The different values of `supp_num` (1 for OJ and 2 for VC) are represented by different symbols in the plot (1 values are represented with a circle, and 2 values are represented with a triangle). You can consider using `mutate()` as an alternative to the method of creating new variables discussed earlier in this chapter.

```
> ToothGrowth_df <- mutate(ToothGrowth_df,
    supp_num=as.numeric(supp))
> attach(ToothGrowth_df)
> plot(len ~ dose,pch=supp_num)
```

HANDLE MISSING DATA

As a data scientist working with enterprise data sets, you'll be surprised (and sometimes frustrated) by the state of the data you receive. Corporate data is often quite dirty because of years of poor data governance. One recurring theme is missing data. It is quite common for some of the records to be incomplete in the sense that certain data fields (features) are missing or in error. We need to validate each record to make sure it contains the same number of fields and that each field contains the type of data we expect. We also need a plan for dealing with missing data. We can discard a whole record if it is incomplete, or we can try to infer the missing values based on the data from other records. A common approach is to fill the missing data with the average or the median of the other data values. This is called *imputing* data values.

To demonstrate one way to handle missing values, we'll use the `iris` data set and selectively set a few data values to `NA` (the way in R to denote a missing value). Then we'll use the `impute()` function in the `e1071` package to set the missing values to the mean of the column. Just a warning that `impute()` returns a matrix, not a data frame, so we must take the extra step of converting the resulting R object `iris_repaired` back to a data frame. Note that the `e1071` package has many useful functions that are of good use to data scientists.

```
> library(e1071)
> iris_missing_data <- iris
> iris_missing_data[5,1] <- NA
> iris_missing_data[7,3] <- NA
> iris_missing_data[10,4] <- NA
> iris_missing_data[1:10, -5]
```

} insert NA

	Sepal.Length	Sepal.Width	Petal.Length	Petal.Width
1	5.1	3.5	1.4	0.2
2	4.9	3.0	1.4	0.2
3	4.7	3.2	1.3	0.2
4	4.6	3.1	1.5	0.2
5	NA	3.6	1.4	0.2
6	5.4	3.9	1.7	0.4
7	4.6	3.4	NA	0.3
8	5.0	3.4	1.5	0.2
9	4.4	2.9	1.4	0.2
10	4.9	3.1	1.5	NA

```
> iris_repaired <- impute(iris_missing_data[,1:4], what='mean')
> iris_repaired <- data.frame(iris_repaired)
> iris_repaired[1:10, -5]
```

	Sepal.Length	Sepal.Width	Petal.Length	Petal.Width
[1,]	5.100000	3.5	1.400000	0.200000
[2,]	4.900000	3.0	1.400000	0.200000
[3,]	4.700000	3.2	1.300000	0.200000
[4,]	4.600000	3.1	1.500000	0.200000
[5,]	5.848993	3.6	1.400000	0.200000
[6,]	5.400000	3.9	1.700000	0.400000
[7,]	4.600000	3.4	3.773826	0.300000
[8,]	5.000000	3.4	1.500000	0.200000
[9,]	4.400000	2.9	1.400000	0.200000
[10,]	4.900000	3.1	1.500000	1.206711

Now let's consider the case where you wish to discard records having missing values in one or more fields. (This might be a valid solution when the number of records being removed is small compared to the total number of records.) The example below shows one method in R for performing the removal using the complete.cases() function.

```
> df <- iris_missing_data   # Make a copy of the data frame
> nrow(df)   # 150 rows including 3 rows with missing data
[1] 150

> iris_trimmed <- df[complete.cases(df[,1:4]),]
> iris_trimmed <- na.omit(df) # This works too
> nrow(iris_trimmed)
[1] 147
```

2 ways to remove the rows w/ NA

Here is another method that might be useful for first determining how many observations have missing values and then deleting them, if deemed appropriate.

```
> df.has.na <- apply(df,1,function(x){any(is.na(x))})
> sum(df.has.na) # Show a count of observations with NA
[1] 3
> iris_trimmed <- df[!df.has.na,] # Remove the observations
```

FEATURE SCALING

One characteristic of numeric data in your list of features that becomes quite apparent early on in the data munging process is the likelihood that the range of numeric values is different between the various feature variables. For example, the number of bedrooms in a single family home may range from one to five, whereas the square footage of the home might range from 1,000 to 3,500 square feet. The different magnitude is due to different measurement units. Feature scaling is the process that allows us to compare numeric features at the same scale; we need to normalize the data by subtracting their average and then divide by the standard deviation. Our goal will be to yield a common numeric range between -1 and 1. Fortunately, R has the scale()

function in the base R `stats` package to scale numeric values. The example below uses the `iris` data set and scales all the numeric variables using `scale()`.

The reason why feature scaling is important centers on how some machine learning algorithms function. For example, many classifiers calculate the distance between two data points. If one of the features has a wide range of values, the distance will be governed by this particular feature. Therefore, the range of all features should be normalized so that each feature contributes approximately proportionately to the final distance.

```
> head(iris)   # Note the range of each feature
     Sepal.Length  Sepal.Width  Petal.Length  Petal.Width  Species
1       5.1           3.5           1.4           0.2        setosa
2       4.9           3.0           1.4           0.2        setosa
3       4.7           3.2           1.3           0.2        setosa
4       4.6           3.1           1.5           0.2        setosa
5       5.0           3.6           1.4           0.2        setosa
6       5.4           3.9           1.7           0.4        setosa
> scaleiris <- scale(iris[, 1:4])
> head(scaleiris)   # Now view the scaled features
       Sepal.Length   Sepal.Width   Petal.Length   Petal.Width
[1,]    -0.8976739     1.01560199    -1.335752      -1.311052
[2,]    -1.1392005    -0.13153881    -1.335752      -1.311052
[3,]    -1.3807271     0.32731751    -1.392399      -1.311052
[4,]    -1.5014904     0.09788935    -1.279104      -1.311052
[5,]    -1.0184372     1.24503015    -1.335752      -1.311052
[6,]    -0.5353840     1.93331463    -1.165809      -1.048667
```

DIMENSIONALITY REDUCTION

Often referred to as "the curse of dimensionality," attempting to work with high-dimension models (i.e., models with a large number of features) is problematic with machine learning algorithms for a number of reasons:

- Performance may be slow when working with many features

- Models with many features may not fit within the memory you have available on the computer you're using since open source R is bound by the amount of memory available.

- It is very difficult to use common visualization techniques when working with more than three features (a three-dimensional plot).

There are two commonly used strategies to reduce the number of features in your model. First, you can remove any irrelevant features. Start by examining all features in the model and consider if each is really contributing to the machine learning task. For example, if your data set includes a Customer Number field, there is no point in keeping this as a feature, since its value is arbitrary in nature. The general approach is to try different combinations of feature subsets to see which combination yields the best performance (how well it predicts using the test data set). As discussed earlier in this chapter in the section on Feature Engineering, start with a small number of features, test their predictive power, and then add more features and repeat the process. You can also try the opposite approach—starting with a full set of features and then removing groups of features while testing their ability to predict.

Typically, keeping irrelevant features in the model will affect the overall performance of the machine learning solution per the three reasons outlined above, but it won't affect the accuracy of the prediction to a great degree. This is a lesser problem than redundant features, which will give unequal weights to information that are redundant. Removing redundant features is a higher priority.

A more nuanced approach for dimensionality reduction involves a process called *Principal Component Analysis* (PCA), which is based on a theoretical element of linear algebra called *Singular Value Decomposition* (SVD). PCA is also an important method for unsupervised machine learning and will be examined in more detail in Chapter 8. For now, we'll take a quick look at PCA in terms of how it can be used during the data munging step. PCA transforms the feature set into a lower dimension space while retaining most of the variance of the original. PCA is not very intuitive until you step through the mathematics, but fortunately R has a useful package containing the prcomp() command that saves you from having to do all that.

Let's explore PCA using the iris data set. The process we'll go through is as follows; the R code is provided as well:

- Use the cor() function in the base R stats package to calculate a correlation matrix using the data frame containing the iris dataset. We also remove the fifth variable, Species, since it is not quantitative.

- Examination of the resulting correlation matrix shows a high correlation between variables Petal.Length and Petal.Width (96%), as well as Petal.Length and Sepal.Length (87%).

- Use the prcomp() function in the base R stats package to compute a principal component analysis on the iris data frame. We use the scale argument, which is generally advisable, to scale the variables to have unit variance. We create a prcomp object called iris_pca.

- Using the summary() function on the iris_pca object, we see the four principal components. We see that the PC1 and PC2 components maintain the most variation, 73% and 23%, respectively.

- We then use the plot() function on the prcomp object iris_pca. The plot in Figure 3-4 shows the relative variance for each of the principal components.

- The iris_pca$rotation command displays a matrix of variable "loadings," e.g., a matrix whose columns contain eigenvectors.

- Now we use the predict() function for the prcomp object and calculate the new reduced dimension data set using the first two principal components.

- Finally, we use the biplot() function in Figure 3-5 to show both the principal component scores and the principal component loadings in a single plot.

This PCA exercise serves as a brief overview of how PCA can reduce the dimension of the iris data set from four to two features. The procedure and the terminology involved will be discussed in greater depth in Chapter 8.

```
> cor(iris[,-5]) # calculate a correlation matrix
             Sepal.Length   Sepal.Width   Petal.Length   Petal.Width
Sepal.Length   1.0000000    -0.1175698     0.8717538      0.8179411
Sepal.Width   -0.1175698     1.0000000    -0.4284401     -0.3661259
Petal.Length   0.8717538    -0.4284401     1.0000000      0.9628654
Petal.Width    0.8179411    -0.3661259     0.9628654      1.0000000
> iris_pca <- prcomp(iris[,-5], scale=T) # compute a principal
      component analysis
> summary(iris_pca)
Importance of components:
                         PC1        PC2        PC3        PC4
Standard deviation      1.7084     0.9560     0.38309    0.14393
Proportion of Variance  0.7296     0.2285     0.03669    0.00518
Cumulative Proportion   0.7296     0.9581     0.99482    1.00000
> plot(iris_pca)
```

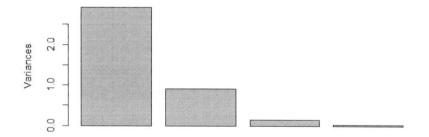

iris_pca

Figure 3-4 PCA plot showing relative variance for each principal component

```
> iris_pca$rotation
                   PC1         PC2          PC3         PC4
Sepal.Length    0.5210659  -0.37741762   0.7195664   0.2612863
Sepal.Width    -0.2693474  -0.92329566  -0.2443818  -0.1235096
Petal.Length    0.5804131  -0.02449161  -0.1421264  -0.8014492
```

"loadings"

```
Petal.Width      0.5648565 -0.06694199 -0.6342727  0.5235971
> predict(iris_pca)[1:2,] # calculate the new reduced dimension data
    set
        PC1        PC2        PC3       PC4
[1,]  -2.257141  -0.4784238  0.1272796 0.02408751
[2,]  -2.074013   0.6718827  0.2338255 0.10266284
> biplot(iris_pca)
```

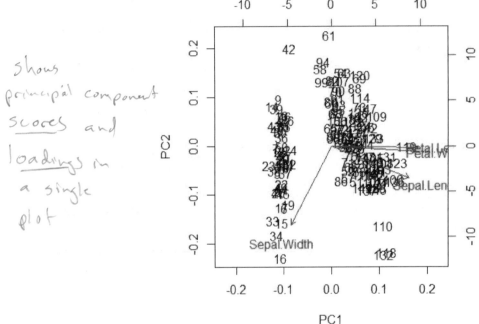

shows
principal component
scores and
loadings in
a single
plot

Figure 3-5 PCA biplot of the first two principal components

SUMMARY

This chapter focused on the part of a machine learning project that often takes the longest period of time to complete: data munging. Individual techniques to address common data munging needs were highlighted. In reality, this is just the tip of the iceberg. There are many other possible requirements such as handling outliers, handling inconsistent values in fields (e.g., a city field might contain LA, L.A., and Los Angeles), power and log transformations, etc. Your job as a data scientist is to build up your data munging toolbox over time as you complete more projects and encounter diverse situations.

The next step in the machine learning process involves performing exploratory data analysis on the now cleansed and organized data set. This is the subject of Chapter 4. With a clean data set, statistical tools will yield much more useful results.

Here is a summary of what you've learned in this chapter:

- Feature engineering is where you take steps to identify the pertinent feature variables to use with machine learning algorithms.
- Data munging is an integral part of the machine learning "data pipeline."
- Random sampling is used to reduce the number of observations in a large data set.
- We started building out a data munging toolbox with a variety of commonly used techniques. You're encouraged to continually add to your own toolbox based on your personal needs. It is a good idea to keep an eye out for new R packages that may address new data munging requirements.
- Dimensionality reduction is used to lower the number of feature variables in your data set while maintaining the same amount of variation.

Chapter 4
Exploratory Data Analysis

Once the laborious task of data munging is complete, the next step in the machine learning process is to become intimately familiar with the data set by performing what's called *Exploratory Data Analysis* (EDA). The way to gain this level of familiarity is to utilize the many features of the R statistical environment that support this effort: numeric summaries, aggregations, distributions, densities, review of all the levels of factor variables, application of general statistical methods, exploratory plots, expository plots, and much more. It is always a good idea to explore a data set with multiple techniques, especially when they can be done together for purposes of comparison. In this chapter, we'll outline a cookbook for techniques in exploratory data analysis. Once you fully understand your data set, it is quite possible that you may need to revisit one or more data munging tasks in order to refine or transform the data even further. The goal of exploratory data analysis is to obtain confidence in your data to a point where you're ready to engage a machine learning algorithm.

Another side benefit of EDA is to refine the selection of features that will be used later for machine learning. Once you gain deep familiarity with your data set, you may need to revisit the feature engineering step if you find the features that you selected do not serve their intended purpose. Moreover, you may discover other features that add to the overall picture the data presents. Once you complete the EDA stage, you should have a firm feature set to use for supervised and unsupervised statistical learning.

In a hurry to get to the machine learning stage, some data scientists either skip the exploratory process entirely or do a very perfunctory job of it. This is a mistake with many implications including generating inaccurate models, generating accurate models but on the wrong data, not creating the right types of variables in data preparation, and using resources inefficiently because only after generating models does it become apparent that perhaps the data is skewed, or has outliers, or has too many missing values, or that some values are inconsistent.

Plots constitute a significant portion of EDA activities. Let's review why we use plots in EDA to communicate information about data:

- **Understand data properties**: It may be too difficult to look at the entire matrix of data for a machine learning project, so looking at plots is a better way of getting an overview of the data.

- **Find patterns in the data**: You can discover new patterns and associations between variables that might have been surprising had you not been able to look at the data in graphical form.

- **Suggest modeling strategies**: Plots can inform you of the kind of modeling strategies to use.

- **Debug analyses**: You can use plots to determine where your statistical modeling may have gone wrong. Remember, much of machine learning is an iterative process, so plots can lend insight for incremental steps.

- **Communicate results**: The ability to communicate results to other people is vital to any machine learning project. Very often, you'll have a story to tell immediately after performing EDA since it is rare that anyone has taken such a deep look at the data up until that point and new insights will start to emerge with the aid of plots. "Data storytelling" is a very important part of machine learning and is an area that requires a very intangible and uncommon talent from the data scientist. Many of the plots resulting from EDA tasks form the basis of this data storytelling.

One type of plot that you won't often see used for EDA is the pie chart, because it involves angle comparisons (judging the relative sizes of pie slices) that are frequently harder to interpret than position comparisons in other plot types such as barplots and boxplots. 3D bar charts are also not frequently used since judging volume comparisons also can be difficult.

NUMERIC SUMMARIES

The first forms of exploration a data scientist may wish to perform on a data set are numeric summaries or aggregations. It often is useful to become familiar with how frequently a particular value occurs in a variable. For example, using the `airquality` data set, let's see all the unique values found for the `Month` variable. We can use R's `unique()` function for this purpose. The function returns all of the unique values for the variable passed as an argument:

```
> unique(airquality$Month)
[1] 5 6 7 8 9
```

You might also wish to count specific unique values for a particular variable in the data set. Although there are a number of ways to achieve this in R, let's use the `sqldf` package we saw briefly in Chapter 2. Here we can use the SQL statement below to obtain the count for a specific value, (11 for Ozone, in this case) and find that the count is 3.

```
> library(sqldf)
> sqldf("select count(Ozone) from airquality where Ozone=11")
      count(Ozone)
1        3
```

Another useful function is `summary()`, which goes through the entire data set and provides a number of summary statistics for each numeric variable: Min, Max, Mean, Median, first quartile, and third quartile. For factor variables, `summary()` shows the count of the most frequently occurring values (less frequent values are counted in the "Other" category).

```
> summary(airquality)
   Ozone              Solar.R            Wind
 Min.   : 1.00     Min.   :  7.0      Min.   : 1.700
 1st Qu.: 18.00    1st Qu.:115.8      1st Qu.: 7.400
 Median : 31.50    Median :205.0      Median : 9.700
 Mean   : 42.13    Mean   :185.9      Mean   : 9.958
 3rd Qu.: 63.25    3rd Qu.:258.8      3rd Qu.:11.500
```

```
   Max.   :168.00    Max.   :334.0        Max.   :20.700
NA's  :37       NA's  :7
Temp              Month             Day
Min.   :56.00     Min.   :5.000     Min.   : 1.0
1st Qu.:72.00     1st Qu.:6.000     1st Qu.: 8.0
Median :79.00     Median :7.000     Median :16.0
Mean   :77.88     Mean   :6.993     Mean   :15.8
3rd Qu.:85.00     3rd Qu.:8.000     3rd Qu.:23.0
Max.   :97.00     Max.   :9.000     Max.   :31.0
```

A group of other R functions can perform many of the elements of summary() individually on a specific quantitative variable: mean() to compute the arithmetic mean, min() to find the minimum value, max() to find the maximum value, range() to return a vector containing both the minimum and maximum value, and quantile() to compute the minimum, lower quartile, median, upper quartile, and maximum values. Notice that we can add the na.rm=TRUE argument to these functions to ignore any NA values found.

```
> mean(airquality$Ozone, na.rm=TRUE) #remove all NAs
[1] 42.12931
> min(airquality$Wind)   # No NAs in this variable
[1] 1.7
> max(airquality$Solar.R, na.rm=TRUE)
[1] 334
> range(airquality$Month)
[1] 5 9
> quantile(airquality$Ozone, na.rm=TRUE)
0%    25%    50%    75%    100%
1.00 18.00 31.50 63.25 168.00
```

Variance is a statistical measure that shows how the quantitative data values are dispersed around the mean. A variance of zero indicates that all the values are identical. Variance is always non-negative. A small variance indicates that the data points tend to be very close to the mean and hence to each other, while a high variance indicates that the data points are very spread out from the mean and from each other. The square root of variance is called the *standard deviation.*

Let's take a couple of examples of computing variance using the `airquality` data set. The first example shows the variance for the `Temp` variable. The second example shows the variance for `Ozone` while removing all `NA` values from the calculation.

```
> var(airquality$Temp)
[1] 89.59133
> var(airquality$Ozone, na.rm=TRUE)
[1] 1088.201
```

R also has the head() and tail() functions to quickly show the first and last six records in the data set, respectively. This is useful just to get a sense of the data without too much effort. These are likely to be the first examinations you will wish to do with a new data set.

```
> head(airquality)
   Ozone   Solar.R  Wind   Temp   Month   Day
1   41     190      7.4    67     5       1
2   36     118      8.0    72     5       2
3   12     149      12.6   74     5       3
4   18     313      11.5   62     5       4
5   NA     NA       14.3   56     5       5
6   28     NA       14.9   66     5       6
```

Many data sets have categorical variables carrying values such as "Male" or "Female" instead of numeric values. These are called "factor" variables in R. One important exploratory task you should perform on most factor variables is to see what values these variables contain. R has the levels() function to achieve this visibility. To demonstrate this feature, let's take the `ToothGrowth` data set and examine the `supp` variable:

```
> levels(ToothGrowth$supp)
[1] "OJ" "VC"
```

When exploring a data set, it is often useful to know how many non-missing values there are for a particular variable. Here are three different methods for doing so in R; the last one is the simplest:

```
> length(airquality$Ozone[is.na(airquality$Ozone) == FALSE])
> length(airquality$Ozone[!is.na(airquality$Ozone)])
> sum(!is.na(airquality$Ozone))
[1] 116
```

EXPLORATORY VISUALIZATIONS

Exploratory visualizations (or plots) are very useful in becoming intimately acquainted with a given data set. Using R's many plotting capabilities, you can often see in an instant what the data are telling you. *Exploratory* plots are those that you might not necessarily save or include in a report; rather, they guide your hand when making early decisions about how to best use your data in machine learning and which model to use. Exploratory graphs are done quickly, typically without regard for how they appear as long as they're able to communicate important information to you, the data scientist. Think of these plots as "rough drafts" for later, final analysis. A large number of exploratory plots are made, and most will be discarded before you perform your final analysis. You make these plots to explore all of the avenues your data might take you. The goal is for personal understanding, not necessarily communication with other people. Don't worry about using an array of colors, titles, legends, axis labels, etc. at this point; aesthetics are not important during the exploratory stage.

Expository plots are a bit different. They are plots that you choose to dress up a bit more to make them presentable to decision makers in your organization or to your clients. These plots can be embedded in a final report of your findings. We'll take a look at them later in the chapter.

HISTOGRAMS

When performing EDA, it's very important to understand the shape of the distribution of the data set. Looking at distributions can tell you if there are outliers in the data, whether a certain machine learning algorithm will work on the data, or simply how many observations are within a certain range of values. A single variable frequency plot, or *histogram*, is a simple but useful tool to quickly gain an understanding of how the values of a particular variable are distributed. The goal is to quantify a single variable distribution of data, so in this sense, it is similar to the boxplot() that we'll see later. Using the iris data set, we'll explore the Sepal.Length variable using a histogram:

```
> hist(iris$Sepal.Length)
```

The plot shown in Figure 4-1 represents the frequency of each value found in the Sepal.Length variable. For example, it shows that there are 5 values out of 150 observations that contain a Sepal.Length value between 4 and 4.5. Based on this, we can see it is different from a barplot, which just shows counts of a specific value of a variable. The nice thing about the histogram versus a boxplot is that you can see the shape of the distribution.

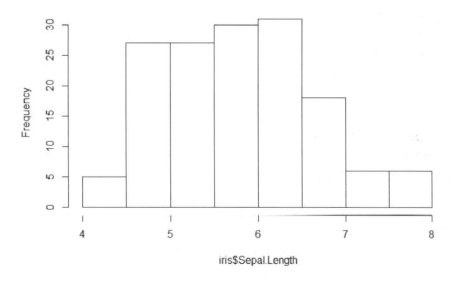

Figure 4-1 Histogram showing frequency of values for Sepal.Length variable

Now let's look at another style of histogram that shows the frequency distribution. We'll do this using the probability=TRUE argument of the hist() function. This form of histogram reports density instead of frequency of values. Think of density as the percentage of the total number of observations that a particular value constitutes. You can also specify the number of breaks in the histogram using the `breaks` argument to increase the granularity in the display. Lastly, we'll add a smooth line showing the density of the distribution using the `lines()` and `density()` functions. The density line, as shown in Figure 4-2, is usually a nice adjunct to a histogram.

```
> hist(iris$Sepal.Length, probability=TRUE, breaks=10)
> lines(density(iris$Sepal.Length))
```

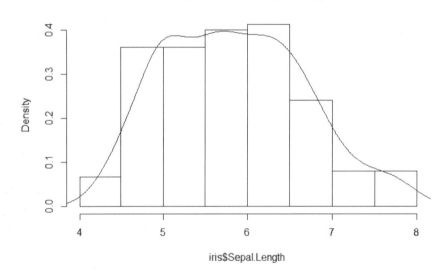

Figure 4-2 Histogram, with smoothing line, showing density of values for `Sepal.Length` variable

BOXPLOTS

The next type of plot we'll discuss is called the *boxplot*. It is particularly good for quantitative variables. The goal of a boxplot is to give you another picture of the distribution of the data. Below is an example of the `boxplot()` function using the `Ozone` variable found in the `airquality` data set. We pass the quantitative variable as an argument along with `col="blue"`, which I tend to use in exploratory plots so the body of the boxplot will appear in a color, rather than black, to more easily distinguish it from the other parts of the plot.

```
> boxplot(airquality$Ozone, col="blue")
```

Let's describe all of the ingredients of the boxplot shown in Figure 4-3. There are several different values encoded in a boxplot. The thick black line in the middle of the body of the plot represents the *median*, or center of the distribution (31.5, as shown on the plot). The median is also known as the second quartile (Q2). The upper and lower bounds of the box represent the 75th (Q3) and 25th (Q1) quartiles of the data, respectively. The length of the rectangle from top to bottom is the interquartile range (IQR). The vertical extensions coming out of the box are called "whiskers," where the upper whisker represents the maximum value or the 75th quartile plus 1.5 times the IQR, whichever is smaller; the lower whisker is the minimum value or the 25th quartile minus 1.5 times the IQR, whichever is larger. You'll see a couple of data points floating above the upper whisker; these represent outliers (there can be outliers below the lower whisker as well).

From reviewing the boxplot, you can see the quantitative distribution of data; i.e., if the data have values spread out or compacted. You can also see if the distribution is symmetric or not by where the mean line falls in the box. If the mean line is close to the center of the box, then the distribution is more symmetric, whereas if the line is pulled toward the top or bottom of the box, then the distribution is more asymmetric. In the example, the distribution of `Ozone` appears to be somewhat asymmetric since the mean line is seen towards the bottom of the box.

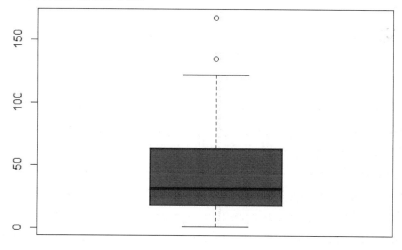

Figure 4-3 Boxplot showing values for `airquailty.Ozone` variable

Boxplots are also good for comparing the distributions of multiple variables on a common scale. By producing the plots on the same scale, we are able to make direct comparisons of medians, quartiles, and inter-quartile ranges. The comparison of medians using boxplots can be regarded as the graphical equivalent of two-sample t-tests and one-way analysis of variance. For example, the `boxplot()` function call below will show the values of `len` from the `ToothGrowth` data set broken down by `supp`. In this case, we get two boxplots since there are only two unique values for `supp`, VC and OJ.

```
> boxplot(ToothGrowth$len ~ as.factor(ToothGrowth$supp), col="blue")
```

The resulting boxplot is shown in Figure 4-4. We see that the mean value of `len` for OJ is higher than the mean for VC. So by putting the boxplots together on the same scale, you can compare the centers of the distribution and also the variability of the distributions.

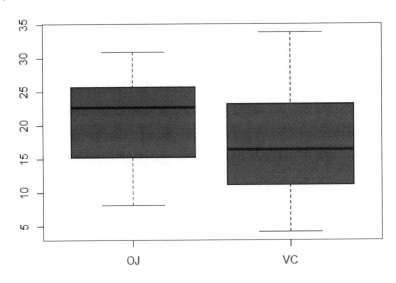

Figure 4-4 Boxplots showing values for `ToothGrowth.len` variable by `supp`

In order to determine the relative number of observations for each category OJ and VC, you can add the `varwidth=TRUE` parameter for `boxplot()`. In this case, the width of each box will be proportional to the number of observations. In the case of our example, the boxes are the same since each category has 30 observations. Note that in this case, we're using different colors for the boxes.

```
> boxplot(ToothGrowth$len ~ as.factor(ToothGrowth$supp),
    col=c("blue","orange"), varwidth=TRUE)
```

BARPLOTS

Another type of plot that's useful for EDA is the *barplot*. Barplots allow you to make comparisons of data values based on position. We use the `barplot()` function in tandem with `table()` that, in this case, is used to come up with a series of counts for each unique value of the `Temp` variable in the `airquality` data set. Here we see that the `Temp` value of 56 is found in one observation, 75 is found in four observations, and 90 is found in three observations. We can use this data for a barplot, as shown in Figure 4-5.

```
> table(airquality$Temp)
```

```
56 57 58 59 61 62 63 64 65 66 67 68 69 70 71 72 73 74 75 76 77 78 79 80 81 82 83 84 85 86 87
 1  3  2  2  3  2  1  2  2  3  4  4  3  1  3  3  5  4  4  9  7  6  6  5 11  9  4  5  5  7  5
88 89 90 91 92 93 94 96 97
 3  2  3  2  5  3  2  1  1
```

```
> barplot(table(airquality$Temp), col="blue")
```

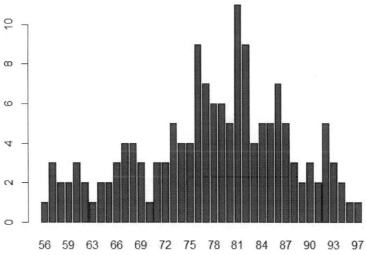

Figure 4-5 Barplot showing distribution of values for the airquality$Temp **variable**

In a barplot, the height of the bar is equal to the count of the data value. This means that at a glance you tell the number of observations in any particular class. In our example, we can quickly determine that the `Temp` value 81 occurs most frequently in the data set. Gaining knowledge of the distribution of your data is very important during the EDA stage of a machine learning project.

DENSITY PLOTS

Another important type of plot for EDA is called a *density plot*. A density plot is like a histogram that's been smoothed out. So instead of a series of vertical bars, we see a curve that represents the density of the distribution. Here is an example of a density plot for the `Temp` variable in the `airquality` data set. We use the `density()` function, which asks R to compute what's called a *kernel density estimation* for the variable. A kernel is a special type of probability density function (PDF) with the added property that it must be even (in addition to being non-negative and real-valued). Some common PDFs are kernels such as uniform and normal distributions. The resulting plot is shown in Figure 4-6.

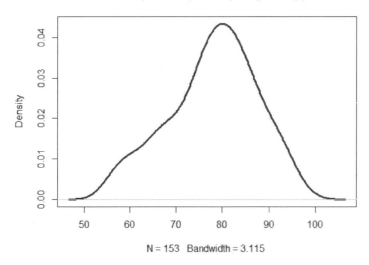

Figure 4-6 Density plot for the values of the `airquality$Temp` variable

```
> temp_dens <- density(airquality$Temp)
> plot(temp_dens, lwd=3, col="blue")
```

Density is a different statistical concept from the frequency we saw in the histogram. So instead of calculating the exact number of temperatures between 0 and 50, we see the percentage of observations between 0 and 50. Even though the plot has been smoothed, you still see the same general shape that the histogram showed although the smoothing process may introduce a small amount of error at the boundary positions. Even though the plot seems to indicate it, we don't actually have temperatures less than 50 or greater than 100. This means that with density plots you need to be careful with making interpretations near the boundaries.

One reason you might wish to use density plots over histograms is that you can overlay multiple distributions on the same plot. To illustrate this concept, we can use the `ToothGrowth` data set and create a density plot for the `len` variable in a manner similar to above. Now we'll go a step further by adding a second density for `len`, but only for observations where the value of `supp` is VC. In the R code below, we use the `which()` function to subset the data set for just the VC observations. In the resulting plot, shown in Figure 4-7, we can easily compare the densities to see that the density for all observations is somewhat different than the subset density.

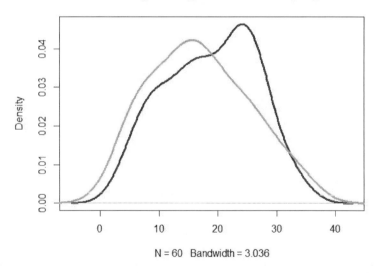

Figure 4-7 Multiple density plot for the values for the `ToothGrowth$len` variable

```
> len_dens <- density(ToothGrowth$len)
> plot(len_dens, lwd=3, col="blue")
> VC_dens <- density(ToothGrowth$len[which(ToothGrowth$supp=="VC")])
```

```
> lines(VC_dens, lwd=3, col="orange")
```

SCATTERPLOTS

The next type of plot we will consider for EDA is the *scatterplot*. The scatterplot is useful in identifying visual relationships between variables and is thus the most commonly used plot for exploratory data analysis. In the R code below, we use the `plot()` function to implement the scatterplot. We use two quantitative variables, `len` and `dose`, from the `ToothGrowth` data set. The `pch` argument specifies the symbol to use for data points on the plot. A value of 19 is for a solid circle, but there are many other possible symbols. The R help statement `?pch` shows the other choices. A side note about scatterplots in R: If there are `NA` values (missing values) in your data set, R will simply not try to plot that data value. If you don't realize this during the exploratory phase, you may jump to incorrect conclusions about your data.

```
> plot(ToothGrowth$len, ToothGrowth$dose, pch=19, col="blue")
```

The resulting scatterplot is shown in Figure 4-8.

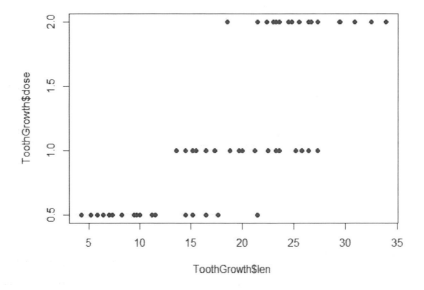

Figure 4-8 Scatterplot comparing the `len` and `dose` variables

On the x-axis is the `len` variable and for the y-axis we have `dose`. Each point on the plot represents one observation. We can see from the plot that values of `dose` are measured in discrete values, namely 0.5, 1.0 and 2.0. You can often pick out patterns once you see the data represented in this manner. Such patterns are instrumental in getting to know your data. One easy pattern to pick out is that tooth length increases with increased dosage. Patterns like this could be very important to the interpretation of the data and how best to model the data set later on in the machine learning process.

With scatterplots, you can also use `col` and `pch` arguments to represent a third variable on the plot. For instance, `col` can be used to selectively color data points to represent a particular value, e.g., we could color data points red where the value of `supp` is "VC" and blue for the "OJ" value. This means that three variables can be represented on the same two-dimensional plot. Alternatively, we can use `pch` to assign different shapes for each data point. Consider the R code below. Here we assign the value 0 (which translates to an open square symbol) to `pch` if the value for `supp` is "VC" and 1 (for an open circle symbol) if `supp` is "OJ." The resulting plot is shown in Figure 4-9.

```
> plot(ToothGrowth$len, ToothGrowth$dose,
     pch=ifelse(ToothGrowth$supp=="VC",0,1), col="blue")
```

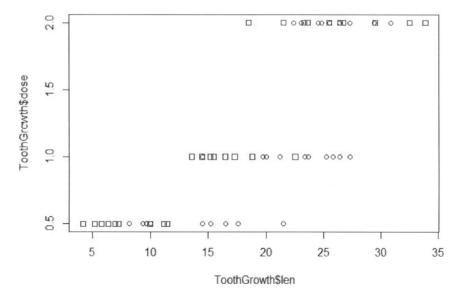

Figure 4-9 Scatterplot comparing the `len` and `dose` variables with `supp` represented

Another example of the scatterplot involves the use of a package called `scatterplot3d`, which enables 3D plotting by placing variables in three dimensions all on one plot. Below is some sample R code that uses the `airquality` data set to plot the `Solar.R` variable on the x-axis, `Wind` on the y-axis, and `Temp` on the z-axis. The resulting 3D plot is shown in Figure 4-10.

```
> library(scatterplot3d)
> scatterplot3d(airquality$Solar.R, airquality$Wind,
    airquality$Temp, highlight.3d=TRUE, col.axis="blue",
    col.grid="lightblue",main="Air Quality Data Set", pch=20,
    xlab="Solar Radiation", ylab="Wind", zlab="Temp")
```

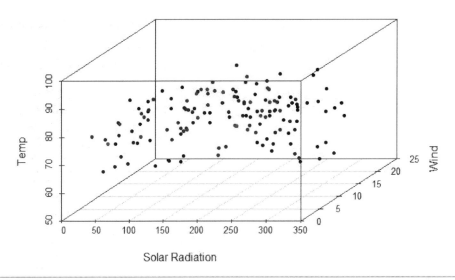

Figure 4-10 3D scatterplot representing airquality variables: Solar Radiation, Temp and Wind

It is a valuable exercise to compute a correlation matrix for quantitative variables in a data set and then produce a scatterplot matrix to visually inspect the correlations. Let's use the `iris` data set to demonstrate this technique. We'll use the `cor()` function in R to compute the correlation matrix.

```
> cor(iris[,c(1,2,3,4)], method="pearson")
             Sepal.Length Sepal.Width Petal.Length Petal.Width
Sepal.Length   1.0000000   -0.1175698    0.8717538    0.8179411
```

Sepal.Width	-0.1175698	1.0000000	-0.4284401	-0.3661259
Petal.Length	0.8717538	-0.4284401	1.0000000	0.9628654
Petal.Width	0.8179411	-0.3661259	0.9628654	1.0000000

The correlation matrix pairs the variables against one another to calculate the correlation between two variables. For example, we see the correlation between `Sepal.Length` and `Petal.Width` is 81.8%, which shows good correlation. Further, `Petal.Length` and `Petal.Width` are highly correlated at 96.3%. Correlation refers to any of a broad class of statistical relationships involving dependence. In the case of R, the Pearson correlation calculation is used by default. However, Kendall and Spearman are also available by changing the `method` argument.

Now let's take a look at the correlation with a scatterplot visualization using the `pairs()` function that produces the plot shown in Figure 4-11. Here we can confirm the correlations exhibited numerically in the correlation matrix.

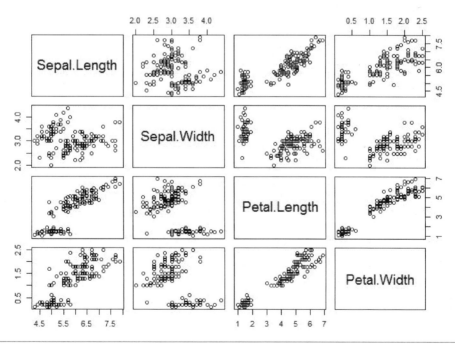

Figure 4-11 Scatterplot matrix for the quantitative variables in the `iris` data set

Locate the subplot for the `Petal.Length` and `Petal.Width` variables. The plot for these two variables show a distinct trend where increased

`Petal.Length` corresponds to increased `Petal.Width`. In contrast, the variables `Sepal.Length` and `Sepal.Width` appear to be negatively correlated at -11.7%. This knowledge can help later on with supervised machine learning.

```
> pairs(iris[,c(1,2,3,4)])
```

We'll wrap up our discussion of scatterplots with a look at exploratory techniques for big data machine learning projects based on large data sets. We'll use a large simulated data set for this purpose. In the R code below, we use the `rnorm()` function to generate two series of random numbers (100,000 each) using a normal distribution. The resulting scatterplot of the two variables is shown in Figure 4-12. It is basically one big lump of points because, as is common with large data sets, most of the points overlay each other, making it impossible to see what's happening in the dense middle area of the plot. Specifically, you won't be able to tell the density of points, i.e., where distinct clumps of points might reside. As a result, we need to try different techniques to find out what's going on with the data.

```
> x <- rnorm(1e5)
> y <- rnorm(1e5)
> plot(x,y, pch=16)
```

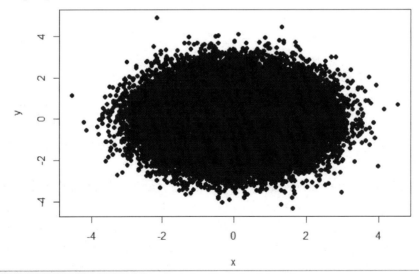

Figure 4-12 An overly dense scatterplot typical of a big data data set

One such technique is to sample the values in the data set. In the R code below, we use the `sample()` function to take a random sample of 1,000 observations without replacement, yielding an integer vector that is used as an index into both x and y. Then we use plot(), with the goal of visualizing one thousand data points. Notice how we subset both x and y over the same sample values indexed by sampledSubset. The resulting plot is shown in Figure 4-13. Now the points are much more distinguishable. You can see the relationship between the two variables even though we're working with a small random sub-sample of the original data set. For exploratory data analysis, you don't need to see all of the points.

```
> sampledSubset <- sample(1:1e5, size=1000, replace=FALSE)
> plot(x[sampledSubset], y[sampledSubset], pch=16)
```

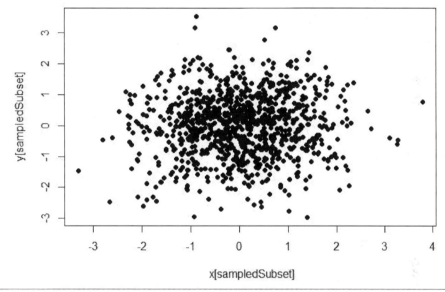

Figure 4-13 Plot of a random sub-sample of 1,000 observations out of 100,000

Another technique for managing a large number of data points is to use the smoothScatter() function, which produces a color smooth density representation of the scatterplot obtained through a kernel density estimate. We can use the entire simulated data set in this case. It shows places where there are many points in darker colors. Figure 4-14 shows the plot. Notice that there are many points in the inner regions and fewer points as you move outward. It also shows outliers as hard dots where they appear on the fringes of the plot. So a smooth scatterplot allows you to visualize the relationships between the variables without having to see all the points themselves.

```
> smoothScatter(x,y)
```

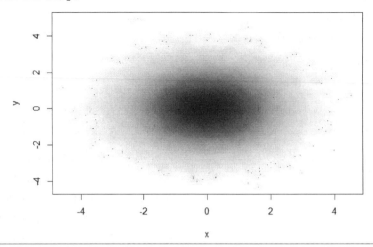

Figure 4-14 Smooth scatterplot of the entire data set

Finally, we can use a technique called "hexagonal binning" to represent a large number of points in a data set. In the R code below, we use the `hexbin` package to create a `hexbin` object using x and y. The plot shown in Figure 4-15 breaks up the x and y values into hexagonal bins and counts the number of points in each bin.

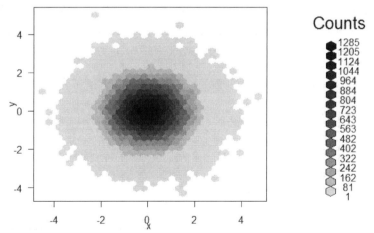

Figure 4-15 Hexagonal binning used to visualize a large number of points.

Once again, darker bins in the plot indicate more points, while lighter colored bins in the outer areas mean fewer points. Using the bin approach allows you to visualize the relationship between x and y when there is a large number of points.

```
> install.packages("hexbin")
> library(hexbin)
> hbins <- hexbin(x,y)
> plot(hbins)
```

QQ-PLOTS

Another type of exploratory plot is called a QQ-plot or quantile-quantile plot. This plot is somewhat similar to a scatterplot in that it is used with quantitative variables. The difference is that it plots the quantiles of one variable against the quantiles of another variable. It is used to visually inspect the similarity between the underlying distributions of two variables. The axes of the plot represent the 1st percentile all the way up to the 100th percentile of the variables. In the R code below, we use a small simulated data set of 50 data points and two variables, x and y. If the two distributions were exactly the same, you'd expect the percentiles to land perfectly on the line drawn on the plot with the abline() function (with intercept of 0 and slope of 1). Instead, in Figure 4-16, we see some variation such as at the top of the plot where the quantiles for y are slightly larger than the quantiles for x.

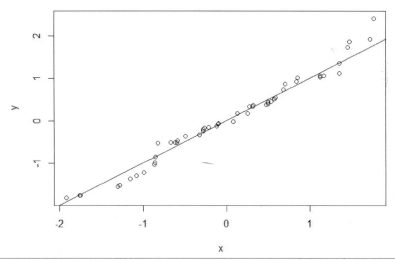

Figure 4-16 QQ-plot of a simulated data set with normally distributed variables

QQ-plots are useful to see if your data are normally distributed.

```
> x <- rnorm(50)
> y <- rnorm(50)
> qqplot(x,y)
> abline(c(0,1))
```

HEATMAPS

Another useful type of exploratory plot is called a *heatmap*, which is sort of like a two-dimensional histogram. Heatmaps are made using the `image()` function. The idea behind the heatmap is to use color intensity to represent how large a data value is, so the brighter the color the larger the value. White depicts the largest value, and red is the smallest value, with different shades of color representing values in between. Using heatmaps, you can visualize an entire matrix of values all in a single plot.

Let's look at an example of a heatmap using the `iris` data set with the R code below. The first argument indicates the rows of a matrix to be used in the plot (observations), and the second argument is for the feature variables. The third argument needs to be a matrix object, so we convert the `iris` data frame to a matrix using the `as.matrix()` function. In this example, the data set is of modest size, so we'll use all 150 observations and all four quantitative variables.

```
> image(1:150, 1:4, as.matrix(iris[1:150, 1:4]))
```

Figure 4-17 shows the resulting heatmap where row 4 has the smallest values and row 1 has the largest values. One thing of note when looking at the heatmap is that the plot is transposed, i.e., the rows of the plot correspond to the feature variables, and columns correspond to the observations. This may be counterintuitive, since we specified rows first and columns second in the `image()` function call. If you so desire, you can always transpose the matrix using the R code below:

```
> transMatrix <- as.matrix(iris[1:150, 1:4])
> transMatrix <- t(transMatrix)[,nrow(transMatrix):1]
> image(1:4, 1:150, transMatrix)
```

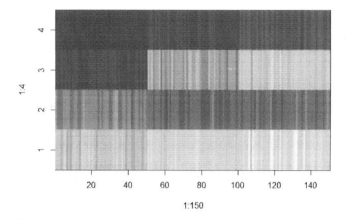

Figure 4-17 Heatmap for the `iris` data set

MISSING VALUE PLOTS

The final exploratory plot we'll consider is a technique for using boxplots to better understand missing values in the data set. Let's take, for example, a variable in the `airquality` data set that has NA values, `Solar.R`. We'd like to explore whether there is a relationship between the missing values in `Solar.R` and the values of `Temp`. To do this, we use the `boxplot()` below, which compares values where `Solar.R` is equal to NA and not equal to NA. So if you look at Figure 4-18, you'll see that when `Solar.R` is equal to NA, the `Temp` values are generally smaller, and when `Solar.R` is not equal to NA, the `Temp` values are generally larger.

```
> boxplot(airquality$Temp ~ is.na(airquality$Solar.R))
```

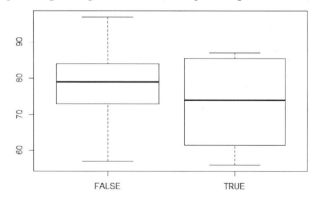

Figure 4-18 Using a boxplot for finding relationships with variables having NA

EXPOSITORY PLOTS

Expository plots are the more formal and permanent versions of the exploratory plots described above. Furthermore, this class of plots is used to communicate results to other people. It may take many iterations of exploratory plots to yield a single expository plot. While exploratory plots are used to discover hidden secrets in your data, expository plots are used to communicate the data's story, and they often find their way into the final reports and results of the machine learning project. Since these plots are part of the permanent record of the project, you'll need to spruce them up with titles, labels, legends, etc. Here is a short list of goals common to expository plots:

- The general goal is to communicate information.

- Information density should be at a level where trying to explain the result in words would not be possible.

- Size and color should be used to communicate information but also for aesthetics.

- These plots should include large, easy-to-read titles, axes, and legends.

Let's take a look at a detailed example using the `airquality` data set and the R code below. Our goal is to produce a single expository plot with two panels. R can stack plot panels in many ways. Using the `par(mfrow=c(1,2))` function, we get one row and two columns of panels, so the plots will appear side-by-side. We then plot the first panel, using a histogram of the `Ozone` variable. We add a label for the x-axis to the plot by using the `xlab` argument (instead of the R expression that's used as a default) and a title for the plot using the `main` argument.

The second plot will be a scatterplot of the `Ozone` and `Temp` variables. We use some special features, such as making the data points heavier with the `cex` argument (to make the more distinguishable), and we also label both axes including text describing the units for each. It is important to include units for all axes in expository plots. Finally, we include a simple legend for the plot using the `legend()` function. Notice that `legend()` takes the coordinates of the upper left-hand corner for where the legend box is to appear as its first two arguments. The resulting expository plot is shown in Figure 4-19. R offers many additional features for beautifying your plots, thus making it possible to provide a very effective and professional presentation.

```
> par(mfrow=c(1,2))
> hist(airquality$Ozone, xlab="Ozone (ppb)", col="blue", main="Ozone
    Frequencies")
> plot(airquality$Ozone, airquality$Temp, pch=16, col="blue",
    cex=1.25, xlab="Ozone (ppb)", ylab="Temperature (degrees F)",
    main="Air Quality - Ozone vs. Temp", cex.axis=1.5)
> legend(125,60,legend="May-Sep 1973", col="blue", pch=16, cex=1.0)
```

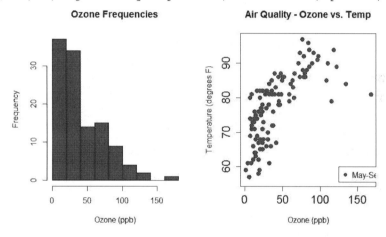

Figure 4-19 Sample expository plots ready for final data science report

SUMMARY

In this chapter, we learned how to perform simple exploratory data analysis to become familiar with our data set. We applied a number of techniques designed to establish a firm understanding of a data set. The next step is to start experimenting with machine learning using a number of algorithms and supervised learning techniques, which will be explored in Chapter 5 and 6.

Here is a summary of what you've learned in this chapter:

- Numeric summaries are very useful to gain insight into the data set being considered for machine learning purposes. We learned how to use tools such as `unique()`, `summary()`, `mean()`, `min()`, `max()`, `range()`, `quantile()`, `var()`, `head()`, `tail()`, `levels()`, and `sum()`.

- Exploratory visualizations are plots that are used to experiment with the data values in a data set in graphical form. Plots can often yield insights not possible by looking at just data values. We learned about some exploratory tools such as histograms, boxplots, barplots, density plots, scatterplots, QQ-plots, heatmaps, and missing value plots.

- Expository visualizations are more formal plots that are often used for final presentations for a machine learning project. These plots are dressed up to best communicate results to others.

Chapter 5
Regression

In this chapter we take the first steps toward applying machine learning methods toward the solution of data science problems. Supervised learning is the most common type of machine learning, often associated with predictive analytics. In demonstrating supervised learning techniques, we'll take a look at many of the most common algorithms such as simple linear regression, multiple linear regression, and polynomial regression. Regression is useful for predicting quantitative values such as sales revenue, home price, rate of inflation, etc. The method has been around for a very long time, and although studying it may seem unexciting compared to some of the other algorithms popular among data scientists, regression is still considered the workhorse of supervised machine learning and is quietly useful and widely used. A firm understanding of regression before studying more complex methods is a good strategy for mastering machine learning techniques. In this chapter, we'll review many key concepts surrounding the regression model.

When examining regression, we should consider a number of important questions about the problem at hand such as:

- Is there a relationship between the variable being predicted and the variable(s) used to make the prediction? Further, how strong is this relationship? Can the prediction be made with a high degree of accuracy?
- Which of the available feature variables contribute to the prediction and how much does each variable contribute? How accurate is the prediction using these feature variables?
- Is the relationship linear?

These questions can be answered through use of regression methods of machine learning. In the sections that follow, we'll take a look at several different orientations for regression that you can place into operation to solve important data science problems.

SIMPLE LINEAR REGRESSION

Linear regression has a long history in the field of statistics and is the most well understood and most popular supervised machine learning algorithm. It is based on the assumption of a linear relationship between the *feature variables* (predictors) and a *response variable* (variable to be predicted). For linear regression, it is assumed that the response variable is quantitative and the predictors are quantitative or qualitative. The algorithm uses a known linear mathematical function (remember high school algebra) to approximate the "unknown" function that generates the observed data. The known function is often called a "hypothesis" function since it is one you choose to approximate the actual, albeit unknown, function. With linear regression, we assume the unknown function is linear. Using the known function, we can use the data set to "fit" or "train" the model. In this case, we need to learn the set of *coefficients* of the hypothesis function, and the most common approach to fitting the model is called *least squares.*

Least squares is determined by adding up the squares of all the error terms. Here, the *error* is simply the difference between the actual response variable value and the predicted value. The reason why we square each error term is to eliminate potential negative error values. The idea is to minimize the least squares, thus making the error as small as possible. R has the lm() algorithm, which we discuss below, that handles the least squares calculations for you.

We do not want to fit the training data perfectly, however, because this could lead to a situation called *overfitting* where the fit obtained will not yield accurate estimates of the response variable on new observations that were not part of the original data set used to train the linear model. We shall discuss the commonly used concept of splitting a data set into training and test portions later in this chapter. For now, we'll use the output of the lm() function for predictive purposes.

Now let's turn to an actual example of simple linear regression using the Boston data set found in the MASS library. This is a data set containing housing values in Boston suburbs; it has 506 observations and 14 variables. We'll use two variables that should have a roughly linear relationship: mdev (median value of owner-occupied homes in $1000s) and rm (the average number of rooms per dwelling). Generally speaking, larger houses with more rooms should command a higher value. We'll try to use linear regression to predict home value using the number of rooms. Both variables are quantitative.

In the code below, we load the MASS library and the Boston data set and then display the names of the variables in the data set.

```
> library(MASS)
> data(Boston)   # 506 obs and 14 variables
> names(Boston)   # Show variables
 [1] "crim"    "zn"     "indus"   "chas"   "nox"      "rm"
 [7] "age"     "dis"    "rad"     "tax"    "ptratio"  "black"
[13] "lstat"   "medv"
```

Next, we use the lm() "linear model" function, which implements the linear regression algorithm in R. lm() has many arguments, but at this point we're only interested in the response variable and the single predictor variable. The argument passed to lm() is the "model formula," or in this case medv~rm, which has the response variable on the left of the tilde ~ (read "is modeled as", "is predicted by", "is dependent on", etc.) and a model specification formula on the right with the predictor variable (in the next section we'll use more than one predictor). For our example, medv~rm can be read as "medv as predicted by rm." Another argument, data=Boston, specifies the data frame where the data resides; this way you don't have to repeat the data frame name, as in Boston$medv~Boston$rm, although this works as well. As with other machine learning algorithms in R, the results of the computation are placed in an object variable—in this case, lm1. Here, lm1 is the linear model fit. If you display this object, you'll see the original function call and the calculated coefficients (intercept and slope).

```
> lm1 <- lm(medv~rm, data=Boston)
> lm1
Call:
```

```
lm(formula = medv ~ rm, data = Boston)
Coefficients:
 (Intercept)        rm
    -34.671      9.102
```

Once you use `lm()` to fit the model to the data, the important question is whether the fit is any good. Will it successfully make predictions? In order to make that determination, you can use the summary() function to get some metrics indicating the quality of the fit. Note that the information found in the linear model object requires an understanding of mathematics and statistics beyond the scope of this book (entire books have been written on the subject). Instead, we'll review some of the basic elements of the linear model object and how to interpret them.

```
> summary(lm1)
Call:
   lm(formula = medv ~ rm, data = Boston)


Residuals:
     Min      1Q  Median      3Q     Max
 -23.346  -2.547   0.090   2.986  39.433


Coefficients:
              Estimate Std. Error t value Pr(>|t|)
(Intercept)   -34.671      2.650  -13.08   <2e-16 ***
rm              9.102      0.419   21.72   <2e-16 ***

 ---
 Signif. codes: 0 '***' 0.001 '**' 0.01 '*' 0.05 '.' 0.1 ' ' 1
Residual standard error: 6.616 on 504 degrees of freedom
Multiple R-squared: 0.4835, Adjusted R-squared: 0.4825
F-statistic: 471.8 on 1 and 504 DF, p-value: < 2.2e-16
```

The use of `summary()` gives us p-values and standard errors for the coefficients, as well as the R^2 statistic and F-statistic for the model. If you wish, you can reference individual components of the linear model summary calculation. In the following discussion, we'll take a look at each component. To start, you can use the ? `summary.lm` command to see what is available.

First, we'll retrieve the coefficients matrix (a parameter table) consisting of four columns: estimated coefficients, standard error of the intercept and slope, t value (Student's t) of the intercept and slope, and p-value for the intercept and slope. Additional rows are added to this matrix when performing multiple linear regression, one row for each additional predictor. A discussion of each column is provided below.

$$t\,value = \frac{\text{Estimate of Coeff.}}{\text{Std Error}} \quad -13.08 = \frac{-34.67}{2.64}$$

```
> summary(lm1)$coefficients
              Estimate Std. Error    t value      Pr(>|t|)
(Intercept) -34.670621  2.6498030  -13.08423  6.950229e-34
rm            9.102109  0.4190266   21.72203  2.487229e-74
```

- The **Estimate** column contains the *estimated coefficients*, i.e., the intercept (the value of medv at rm = 0) and slope (the change in medv per unit change in rm).

- The **Std. Error** column contains the *standard error* of the coefficient estimate about the regression line (often denoted by SE), which is the measure of the variability in the estimate for the coefficient, i.e., the average amount that the regression equation over- or under-predicts. Lower means better, but this number is relative to the value of the coefficient. As a rule of thumb, you'd like this value to be at least an order of magnitude less than the coefficient estimate. In our example the standard error for the rm variable is 0.42, which is 22 times less than the estimate of the coefficient 9.1.

- The **t value** column provides the *t statistic* (also known as the "Student's t-test") of the coefficient estimate. It provides a score that measures whether or not the coefficient for this variable is meaningful for the model. It shows you the t-test associated with testing the significance of the parameter listed in the first column (intercept or slope). For example, the t value of -13.08 refers to the t-test of the (Intercept) -34.671 divided by the standard error of that estimate,

2.650. You probably won't use this value itself, but just know that it is used to calculate the p-value and the significance levels.

- **Pr(>|t|)** is known as the *variable p-value* that gives you the p-value for that t-test (the proportion of the t distribution at that df (degrees of freedom) which is greater than the absolute value of your t statistic). It is the probability the variable is NOT relevant. You want this number to be as small as possible. If the number is very small, R will display the p-value number in scientific notation as in the example, 6.95e-34 (6.95 x 10^{34}).

Here is a slightly different notation to retrieve the standard error column of the coefficients component in the linear model object.

```
> summary(lm1)$coefficients[,2]
(Intercept)        rm
 2.6498030   0.4190266
```

Next, we'll retrieve the *residuals*. The residuals are the difference between actual values of the variable you're predicting (medv) and the predicted values from your regression. For most regressions you want your residuals to look like a normal distribution when plotted. If the residuals are normally distributed, this indicates the mean of the difference between the predictions and the actual values is close to 0, and that is desirable. The residuals component of the linear model is a numeric vector having a length equal to the number of observations in the data set; in this case, 506. Since the vector is so long, we'll only show the first 20 residuals below.

```
> summary(lm1)$residuals[1:20]
1          2          3          4          5          6          7
-1.175745 -2.174021  3.9719677  4.3740621  5.8178479  4.844060  2.848741
8          9          10         11         12         13         14
 5.5924041 -0.083354 -1.078441 -8.373528 -1.123952  2.768301  0.922174
15         16         17         18         19         20
-2.615835  1.4689170  3.7496040 -2.351012  5.2095142  0.742842
```

Next, we'll retrieve the *R-squared* value with `r.squared`. R-squared is the metric for evaluating the goodness of fit of your model. This is a number between 0 and 1. The quality of fit increases with R-squared, with 1 being the best. R-squared is the percent of the total variation in the response variable `medv` that is explained by the model. It is called R-squared because in a simple regression model it is just *the square of the correlation* between the predictor and response variables. In our example, 48% of the cause for `medv` is due to `rm`. One caveat is that while a high R-squared indicates good correlation, correlation does not always imply causation.

```
> summary(lm1)$r.squared
[1] 0.4835255
```

$$R^2$$

Next, we'll retrieve the *residual standard error* (RSE) with `sigma`. RSE is the standard deviation of your residuals. You would like for this number to be proportional to the quantities of the residuals. For a normal distribution, the 1st and 3rd quantiles should be 1.5 +/- the standard error. When RSE is exactly 0, then the model fits the data perfectly (likely due to overfitting). When using `summary()`, *degrees of freedom* is reported along with RSE. The degrees of freedom is the difference between the number of observations included in the training sample and the number of variables used in your model (intercept counts as a variable), so in this case 506-2=504.

```
> summary(lm1)$sigma    # RSE
[1] 6.61616
```

Lastly, we'll retrieve the F-statistic. A *statistical F-test* is performed on the model. This is a numeric vector of length 3 containing the values F ratio, the number of degrees of freedom in the model (i.e., in the numerator `numdf`), and the residual degrees of freedom (i.e., in the denominator `dendf`). This test takes the parameters of our model (in our case, we only have one) and compares it to a model that has fewer parameters. In theory, the model with more parameters should fit better. A value for F-statistic close to 1 means there is no relationship between the response and predictor. On the other hand, a value greater than 1 means there is a relationship. Our example shows a value of 472, so we can infer that `medv` and `rm` are related. When using `summary()`, F-statistic includes DF, or degrees of freedom. This pertains to how many variables are in the model. In our example, there is one variable so there is one degree of freedom. Also included is the p-value where the F-test has a high p-value when the model with more parameters (your model) fails to perform better than the model with fewer parameters. There probably is not a significant boost if this is the case. If the model with more parameters is better than the model with fewer parameters, you will see a lower p-value.

```
> summary(lm1)$fstatistic
     value     numdf     dendf
  471.8467    1.0000 504.0000
```

506-2 = 504

deg of freedom

In the summary() display you'll also see some *significance stars* in the coefficients table, and following the table you'll see the *significance codes legend*. Consider the display from our example:

```
Coefficients:
              Estimate Std. Error t value Pr(>|t|)
(Intercept)   -34.671      2.650  -13.08   <2e-16 ***
rm              9.102      0.419   21.72   <2e-16 ***

  ---
  Signif. codes:  0 '***' 0.001 '**' 0.01 '*' 0.05 '.' 0.1 ' ' 1
```

The stars are shorthand for significance levels, with the number of asterisks displayed according to the p-value computed. *** is used to indicate high significance, and * indicates low significance. In our example, *** indicates that it's unlikely that NO relationship exists between medv and rm. As far as the significance legend goes, the more punctuation there is next to your variables, the better. Blank is bad, dots are pretty good, stars are good, and more stars are very good.

We can use names(lm1) to find out what other pieces of information are stored in the model. For this introduction to linear regression, we are primarily interested in fitted.values, coefficients, and residuals.

```
> names(lm1)    # Show all calculations by lm()
[1] "coefficients"  "residuals"      "effects"      "rank"
[5] "fitted.values" "assign"         "qr"           "df.residual"
[9] "xlevels"       "call"           "terms"        "model"
```

Now let's see the various ways we can access the calculated components of the fitted model.

There are several ways to access each component:

- *Fitted values* are predicted by the model for the values of the predictor variables included (feature variables). You can access the fitted values of the model using `fitted(lm1)`, `lm1$fitted.values`, or `lm1$fitted`. This component of the linear model is a numeric vector with a length equal to the number of observations in the data set—in this case, 506.

- *Coefficients* are the estimate parameters from the model. You can access the coefficients of the model using `coef(lm1)`, `lm1$coefficients`, or `lm1$coef`. This component of the linear model is a numeric vector with a length equal to 1 plus the number of predictors—in this case, 2.

- *Residuals* are the differences between the actual (measured) and predicted values of the response variable—in this case, medv. You can access the residuals of the model using `resid(lm1)`, `lm1$residuals`, or `lm1$resid`. This component of the linear model is a numeric vector with a length equal to the number of observations in the data set—in this case, 506.

For a few examples of the convenient notation above, you can display the coefficients of the linear model using `coef(lm1)`, `lm1$coefficients`, or `lm1$coef`. Note that two values are shown, the intercept and the slope.

```
> coef(lm1)
> lm1$coefficients
> lm1$coef
(Intercept)              rm
 -34.670621      9.102109
```

Using R's data plotting capabilities, we can visualize the linear model using the following commands. We'll use the attach() function in order to place the `Boston` data set in the R search path so we don't need to keep repeating the data set name in the `plot()` and `lines()` functions.

```
> attach(Boston)  # Attach data set so only variable name
> plot(rm, medv, pch=20, xlab="Avg. # Rooms", ylab="Median Value")
> lines(rm, lm1$fitted, lwd=3)
```

The plot in Figure 5-1 shows data points for pairs of `rm` and `medv` along with a regression line drawn in using the fitted values to show the best fit.

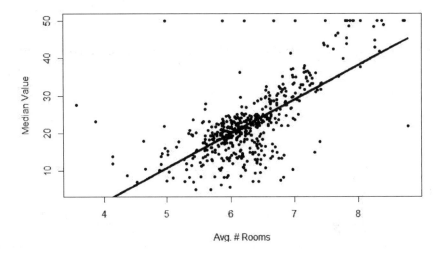

Figure 5-1 Scatterplot of the linear regression model for medv and rm with regression line

Now you can use the coefficients and the trained model to make predictions for new data (not data from the Boston data set). Let's say you want to predict the median home value based on the average number of rooms—6, in this case. In the line of code below, we extract out the first coefficient using `coef(lm1)[1]` and add to it the second coefficient `coef(lm1)[2]` multiplied by 6. Here, we see the predicted median home value is $19,942.

```
> coef(lm1)[1] + coef(lm1)[2]*6
(Intercept)
  19.94203
```

Here is another way of making a prediction, this time using the `predict()` function for the linear model `lm1`. We need to pass a data frame as an argument containing the `rm` value of 6. We get the same predicted median home value as before.

```
> newdata <- data.frame(rm=6)
> predict(lm1, newdata)
1
19.94203
```

Finally, let's look at some diagnostic plots provided by the linear model in conjunction with the `plot()` function as shown in Figure 5-2. When used with a linear model object, `plot()` produces a set of four plots: residuals versus fitted values, a **Q-Q** plot of standardized residuals, a scale-location plot (square roots of standardized residuals versus fitted values), and a plot of residuals versus leverage that adds bands corresponding to Cook's distances of 0.5 and 1.

```
> par(mfrow=c(2,2))   # Split display into 2x2 panel grid
> plot(lm1)
```

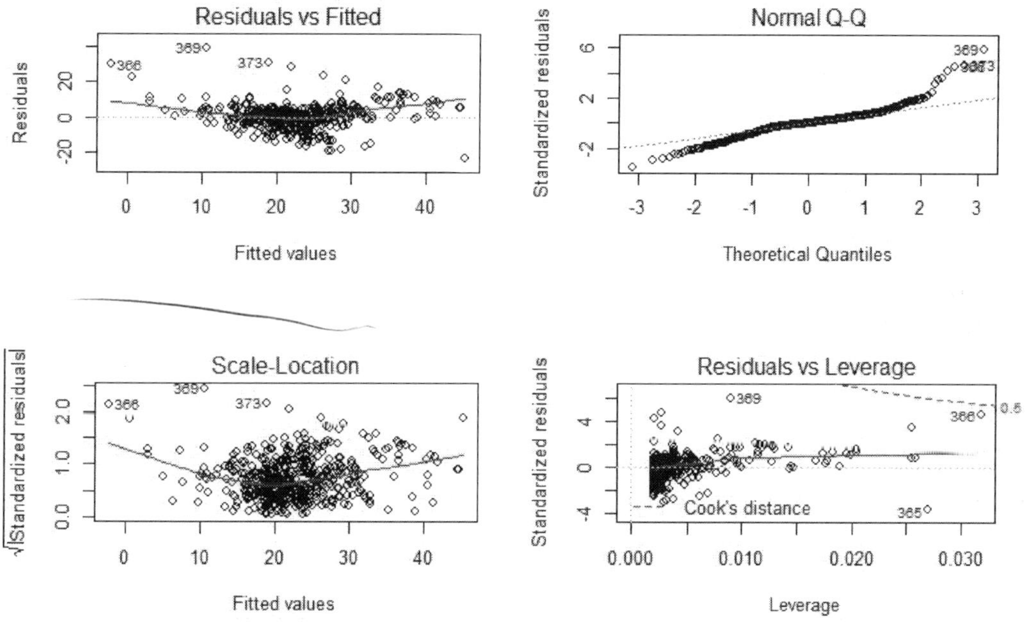

Figure 5-2 Diagnostic plots for the linear regression model for medv and rm

Let's take a closer look at the plots, as a data scientist can use them to determine the model's behavior in making predictions. The first plot is a standard residual plot showing residuals against fitted values. Points that tend toward being outliers are labeled (see point 366 with a value 29.75, point 369 with a value 39.43, and point 373 with a value 31.19). If any pattern is apparent in the points on this plot, then the linear model may not be appropriate. The second plot is a normal quantile plot of the residuals. We like to see the residuals normally distributed. The last plot shows residuals vs. leverage. Labeled points on this plot represent cases we may want to investigate as possibly having undue influence on the regression relationship. Point 366 is one perhaps worth examining further.

Below, we'll display the 366th observation and find the values mdev=27.5 and rm=3.56. But notice that the fitted value for this observation is -2.258, so the residual is quite large at 29.758. The RSE for the model can be retrieved using summary(lm1)$sigma and can then be used to calculate the standardized residual for observation 366, which should be small.

```
> Boston[366,]  # mdev=27.5 rm=3.56
crim zn indus chas  nox  rm age  dis rad tax ptratio
366 4.55587 0 18.1  0 0.718 3.561 87.9 1.6132 24 666   20.2
black lstat medv
366 354.7 7.12 27.5
> lm1$fitted[366]
[1] -2.258
> lm1$residuals[366]
[1] 29.758
> summary(lm1)$sigma   #RSE - residual standard error
[1] 6.61616
> lm1$residuals[366]/summary(lm1)$sigma
   366
 4.497777
```

A commonly used measure of influence is *Cook's Distance*, shown in Figure 5-3. Cook's Distance can be visualized for all the observations in the model using the plot() function below. This measure can be used to estimate the influence of a data point when performing a regression analysis. Specifically, it can indicate data points that are particularly worth checking for validity and indicate regions of the data set where it would be good to be able to obtain more data points. Cook's Distance measures the effect of deleting a given observation. Data points with large residuals (outliers) and/or high *leverage* (identifying those observations that are far away from corresponding average predictor values) may distort the outcome and accuracy of a regression. Points with a large Cook's distance are considered to merit closer examination in the analysis.

```
> par(mfrow=c(1,1))
> plot(cooks.distance(lm1))
```

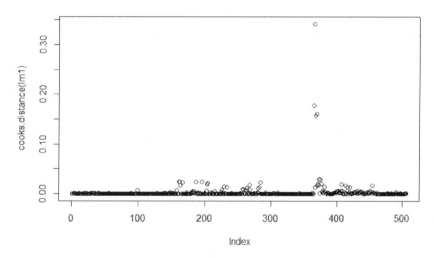

Figure 5-3 Cook's Distance plot for the linear model

We can also directly compute the residuals from the linear regression fit using the residuals() function, as in the plot shown in Figure 5-4 where the residuals are on the y-axis and the predicted responses (fitted value) are on the x-axis. This style of residuals plot is also used with multiple linear regression, to be discussed in the next section. To simplify this plot for simple linear regression, you can plot the residuals versus the predicted (fitted) values. The plot is used to detect non-linearity, unequal error variances, and outliers. Any data point that falls directly on the estimated regression line has a residual of 0. Therefore, the residual = 0 line corresponds to the estimated regression line.

A "well-behaved" residuals plot should exhibit the following behavior:

- The residuals "bounce randomly" around the 0 line. This suggests that the assumption that the relationship is linear is reasonable.

- The residuals roughly form a "horizontal band" around the 0 line. This suggests that the variances of the error terms are equal.

- No one residual "stands out" from the basic random pattern of residuals. This suggests that there are no outliers.

In general, you want your residual vs. fitted values plots to look something like the plot below. Just remember that interpreting these plots is subjective, so try not to over-interpret them by looking at every nuance as something potentially troublesome. You'll especially want to be careful about putting too much weight on residuals vs. fitted values plots based on small data sets. Sometimes the data sets are just too small to make interpretation of a residuals vs. fitted values plot worthwhile.

Residuals plots are a useful visualization tool for identifying non-linearity. Ideally, the residual plot will show no noticeable pattern. On the basis of the residuals plot for lm1, there may be some evidence of non-linear associations in the data.

```
> par(mfrow=c(1,1))
> plot(predict(lm1), residuals(lm1))
```

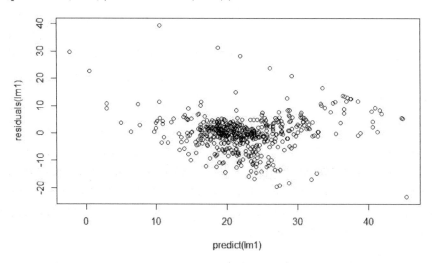

Figure 5-4 Residuals vs. fitted values plot for the linear regression fit

Before we take a look at multiple linear regression, we should mention the situation with outliers. An *outlier* is a data point where the actual value of the response variable is far from the value predicted by the linear model. You can easily detect outliers once you plot the least squares regression line; with respect to the response variable and the predictor, they're generally significantly off the regression line. You can try to remove the observation containing the outlier data point to see how the change affects the coefficients and the resulting regression line. Even if removing an outlier has little effect on the least squares fit, it can cause significant differences in RSE and R^2. You can also use a residual plot to identify outliers and then be careful in deciding how large a residual needs to be for the point to be considered an outlier. If you believe that an outlier was due to an error in data collection, then you can consider removing the observation.

MULTIPLE LINEAR REGRESSION

Although often useful, simple linear regression is only able to make predictions based on a single feature variable. For real life problems, however, we often have more than one predictor. Let's now extend the notion of linear regression to multiple feature variables.

We can use the same least squares approach that we used in the simple linear regression case—finding the coefficients to minimize the sum of squared residuals. We'll use R's lm() algorithm once again to find the multiple least squares regression coefficient estimates. R easily handles the multiple linear regression case by computing the same linear model data we saw in the previous section.

When performing multiple linear regression, we are normally interested in answering some important questions about the model: (i) is there a relationship between the response variable and the predictors; (ii) what are the most important predictors; (iii) considering a set of predictor values, what response value should be predicted and how accurate is the prediction; and (iv) how well does the model fit the data?

We can take a look at multiple linear regression using an example based on the Prestige data set available from the car package. We'll start by installing the `car` package and then loading the library and the `Prestige` data set.

```
> install.packages("car")
> library(car)
> data(Prestige)
```

As always, we should use `summary()` and `head()` to become familiar with the data set.

```
> summary(Prestige)
   education            income              women              prestige
 Min.   : 6.380   Min.    :  611    Min.    : 0.000    Min.    :14.80
 1st Qu.: 8.445   1st Qu.: 4106    1st Qu.: 3.592    1st Qu.:35.23
 Median :10.540   Median :  5930   Median :13.600    Median :43.60
 Mean   :10.738   Mean    : 6798   Mean    :28.979    Mean    :46.83
 3rd Qu.:12.648   3rd Qu.: 8187    3rd Qu.:52.203    3rd Qu.:59.27
 Max.   :15.970   Max.    :25879   Max.    :97.510    Max.    :87.20
     census            type
 Min.   :1113     bc   :44
 1st Qu.:3120     prof :31
 Median :5135     wc   :23
 Mean   :5402     NA's : 4
 3rd Qu.:8312
 Max.   :9517
> head(Prestige)
                      education income women prestige census type
gov.administrators      13.11   12351 11.16     68.8    1113 prof
general.managers        12.26   25879  4.02     69.1    1130 prof
accountants             12.77    9271 15.70     63.4    1171 prof
purchasing.officers     11.42    8865  9.11     56.8    1175 prof
chemists                14.62    8403 11.68     73.5    2111 prof
physicists              15.64   11030  5.13     77.6    2113 prof
```

The Prestige data set contains 102 observations of Canadian occupations including six feature variables. We will use multiple linear regression to predict the `prestige` response variable, an occupation score from a social survey, using the other feature variables as predictors.

The next section of code is important to understand as it reflects a critical element of machine learning—defining the *training set* and *test set* for use by the algorithm. The separation of your data set into a training portion and a test portion is the way the algorithm learns. You split up your data set containing known response variables into two pieces. The training set is used to train the algorithm by calculating the coefficients. Then you use the trained model on the test set to predict the response variables that are already known. The final step is to compare the predicted responses against the observed (actual) responses to see how close they are. The difference is the test error metric. Depending on the test error, you can circle back and refine your model and repeat the process. Once you're satisfied with your model, you can see how well your model "generalizes" by using completely new data.

Let's take a moment here to drill down a little further into the concept of generalization. In machine learning, you need to consider the concept of "in sample" error versus "out of sample" error. The *in sample error* is the error rate you get on the same data set you used to build your predictor. This is sometimes called the resubstitution error. The in sample error is always going to be a little optimistic for the error you would get on a new sample. The reason is that sometimes your predictor will tune itself to the noise in that particular training data set. So when you try a new data set, there will be different noise and the accuracy will go down. The *out of sample error*, in contrast, is the error rate you get on a new data set. This is sometimes called the *generalization error*. This metric gives you a realistic estimation of how well the machine learning algorithm will perform on new data. The out of sample error is what you care about, and the in sample error is always going to be less than the out of sample error.

When splitting your data set, you typically take a majority of the observations and place them in the training set. What's left over goes to the test set. Data scientists typically use a 60-40% split. In the code below, we create two new data frames, `trainPrestige` and `testPrestige`. We also need to remove observations in the `Prestige` data set that are incomplete since there are a few observations with the value `NA` for the `prof` variable.

```
> Prestige_noNA <- na.omit(Prestige)        remove NA rows
> n <- nrow(Prestige_noNA) # Number of observations
> ntrain <- round(n*0.6)  # 60% for training set
> set.seed(333)       # Set seed for reproducible results
> tindex <- sample(n, ntrain) # Create an index
> trainPrestige <- Prestige_noNA[tindex,] # Create training set
> testPrestige <- Prestige_noNA[-tindex,] # Create test set
```

Split data

Let's do some quick exploratory data analysis on the training set so we may become further acquainted with the data. We can plot the response variable against several of the other predictors. We see that there is a trend with the `education` variable shown in Figure 5-5.

```
> plot(trainPrestige$prestige, trainPrestige$education) #Trend
> plot(trainPrestige$prestige, trainPrestige$income)   #No trend
> plot(trainPrestige$prestige, trainPrestige$women)    #No trend
```

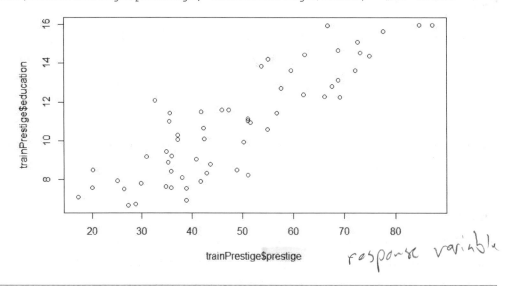

response variable

Figure 5-5 Exploratory data analysis on training set shows a trend

In the code below, `trainPrestige` is used in the linear model function `lm()` for linear regression to calculate the coefficients and other model parameters.

Notice the formula used in `lm()` is of the form: `prestige~.` which means to use all of the other variables as predictors. The `summary()` function includes results for each predictor in the same manner as the single predictor in the simple regression case. In particular, there is an associated p-value that gives the confidence of each estimated coefficient. For example, features not marked with at least one asterisk can be safely ignored. In the model under consideration, `education` and `income` have a high influence to predicting `prestige`.

```
> lm2 <- lm(prestige~., data=trainPrestige)
> summary(lm2)
Call:
 lm(formula = prestige ~ ., data = trainPrestige)
Residuals:
     Min        1Q    Median        3Q       Max
 -13.7864   -4.0290    0.8807    4.5369   16.9482


Coefficients:
               Estimate Std. Error t value Pr(>|t|)
(Intercept) -1.544e+01  9.901e+00  -1.560  0.12492
education    4.562e+00  8.320e-01   5.483 1.24e-06 ***
income      9.607e-04  3.204e-04   2.999  0.00415 **
women       7.252e-03  4.543e-02   0.160  0.87379
census      1.031e-03  7.390e-04   1.396  0.16876
typeprof    5.981e+00  5.773e+00   1.036  0.30495
typewc     -1.137e+00  3.962e+00  -0.287  0.77531
---
Signif. codes:  0 '***' 0.001 '**' 0.01 '*' 0.05 '.' 0.1 ' ' 1
Residual standard error: 7.145 on 52 degrees of freedom
Multiple R-squared:  0.8406,   Adjusted R-squared:  0.8222
F-statistic: 45.71 on 6 and 52 DF,  p-value: < 2.2e-16
```

Once you obtain a fitted linear model, you should run some diagnostic plots to more fully understand the results. One important plot is fitted values (predictions from our model on the training set) versus residuals (amount of variation left over after you've fit your model) to confirm you have a good distribution around the 0 residuals line. The plot in Figure 5-6 shows a cloud distribution that verifies this to be true. There does not appear to be any non-linearity in the model since there is little pattern in the residuals plot. If you find a distinct group of outliers in this plot, you'll want to explore one or more predictors that might be able to explain the outliers.

```
> plot(lm2$fitted, lm2$residuals)
```

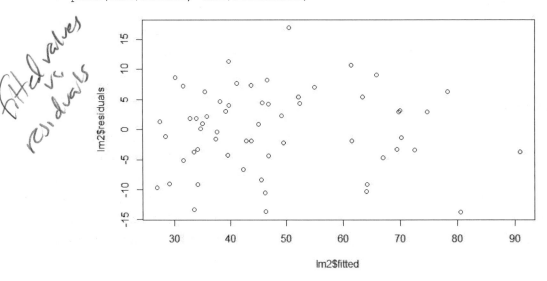

Figure 5-6 The predicted vs. residual plot confirm a good distribution

Another diagnostic technique is to plot the residuals versus the index. (The index refers to the row numbers in the data indicating the particular order in which the data was created) The idea is to check whether there is any sort of unwarranted trend with the index. We can do this with the following plot() command. The plot in Figure 5-7 shows there is no trend.

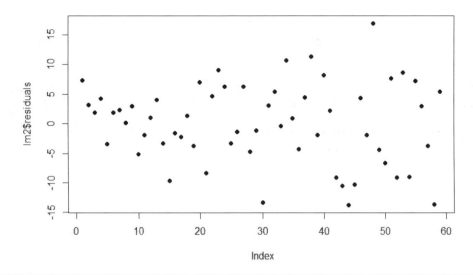

Figure 5-7 Index plot shows no trend

If you detect a distinct trend or set of outliers (e.g. some of the residuals bunched up in an identifiable sequence of index numbers) with respect to the row numbers, it may mean that there is a predictor missing from the model. (In general, a plot of residuals (which is the difference between the actual and fitted values) should not have any relationship to the order of the observations in the data set unless there is a possible relationship with time, age, or some other continuous variable by which the rows are ordered.

```
> plot(lm2$residuals,pch=19)
```

Next, we'll use `testPrestige` to predict the response variable `prestige` (whose values are already known). The idea is to predict something that's already known in order to determine the test error so when you use new data where the response variable is unknown, the predictions will be more accurate.

```
> predict2 <- predict(lm2, newdata=testPrestige)
```

In order to see how accurate our prediction of the test set is, we can use the `cor()` function to establish statistical correlation. Here, we compare predicted values of `prestige` with actual values and get 0.915, which is close to 1 so we can conclude that they are positively linearly related.

```
> cor(predict2, testPrestige$prestige)
[1] 0.9151361
```

Using another diagnostic technique, let's verify if the residuals are normally distributed by displaying a quantile-quantile (Q-Q) plot using the `qqnorm()` and `qqline()` functions. The plot in Figure 5-8 below shows how the residuals are aligned with the normal distribution. Q-Q plots compare the distribution of the sample data (in this case, residuals of the linear model) to the distribution of a theoretical distribution (here, a normal distribution). If the residuals are distributed the same way as the normal distribution, all points will be plotted on a 45-degree line from the lower-left corner to the upper-right corner. Systematic deviations from the line indicate departures from normality such as heavy tails or skewness. If the residuals were normally distributed, they should be closely scattered around the line.

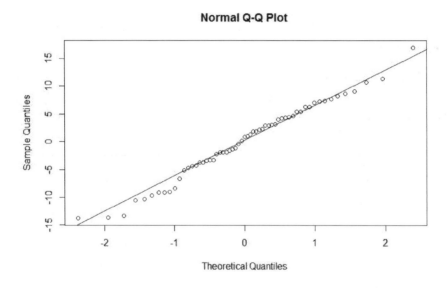

Figure 5-8 A Q-Q plot showing how well the residuals conform to a normal distribution

Remember, residuals are estimates of experimental error obtained by *subtracting the observed responses from the predicted responses*. Examining residuals is a key part of all machine learning. Carefully looking at residuals can tell us whether our assumptions are reasonable and our choice of model is appropriate. Residuals can be thought of as elements of variation unexplained by the fitted model. Since this is a form of error, we expect them to be (roughly) normally and (approximately) independently distributed with a mean of 0 and some constant variance. In our case, we see that the residuals are normally distributed.

```
> rs <- residuals(lm1)
> qqnorm(rs)    # Quantile-quantile plot
> qqline(rs)
```

As a sort of post-mortem, one final diagnostic on the multiple linear regression model we've created is to produce a plot using a variable not used in the model. In the code below, a plot is generated as shown in Figure 5-9. We plot the prestige variable in the test set, versus the predicted values in the test set. Ideally, we'd like to roughly see a 45-degree straight line where prestige was exactly equal to our predictions (though it doesn't always work out that way). In the test set, you can try to identify trends that you may have missed, so we include a new variable in the plot, namely type. Here, type is a categorical variable indicating the type of occupation. It has the following possible values: bc, prof, and wc.

```
> plot(testPrestige$prestige,predict2, pch=c(testPrestige$type))
> legend('topleft', legend=c("bc", "prof", "wc"), pch=c(1,2,3),
    bty='o')
```

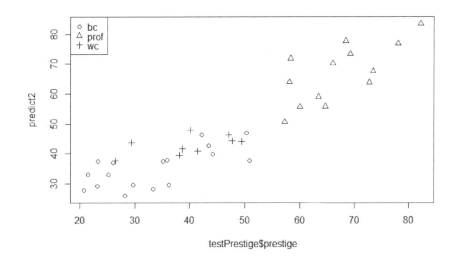

Figure 5-9 A final diagnostic plot for analyzing the multiple linear regression model

POLYNOMIAL REGRESSION

Another useful supervised machine learning technique is called *polynomial regression*, which extends the linear model by adding extra predictors. These extra predictors are obtained by raising each of the original predictors to a power. This algorithm handles non-linear relationships between the response variable and the predictors. You might discover such a non-linear relationship when, while doing exploratory data analysis, a scatterplot reveals a pattern that seems not so linear. If this is the case, polynomial regression can be used to explore a predictor at different levels of *curvilinearity*. As we'll see below, polynomial regression can be used in a hierarchical fashion to best represent a data set. As an example, let's use the `Boston` data set and examine the scatterplot shown in Figure 5-10 of two variables: `nox` and `dis`. The plot demonstrates that these data may not be linear. Notably, for values of `dis` between 6 and 12, the corresponding `nox` values are relatively flat. However, for `dis` values less than 6, `nox` rises in a non-linear fashion. These characteristics suggest that the data is curvilinear.

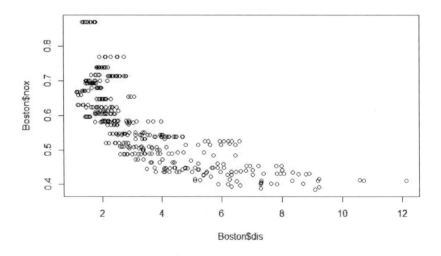

Figure 5-10 A scatterplot showing data is curvilinear.

A general way to address this kind of relationship is to consider a statistical regression situation with one predictor variable: X. An extension of this is a cubic regression using three variables, X, X^2, and X^3, as predictors. This is called a polynomial of *degree* 3. The polynomial approach provides a simple way to provide a non-linear fit to the data. Since any statistical model is merely an approximation, in principle, you can get more accurate models by fitting polynomials of increasingly higher degrees. At some point, however, the model becomes overfit (a topic for Chapter 7), so that the prediction of new, future data actually deteriorates using polynomials of a degree higher than some limit value.

For large enough degrees, a polynomial regression allows us to produce an extremely non-linear curve. Generally, however, it is unusual to use degrees higher than three or four because for higher degree polynomials, the resulting curve can become overly flexible and take on some very strange shapes that might match the training set too closely.

Let's take a look at an example of polynomial regression using the `Boston` data set. We'll fit a linear model using the `lm()` function in order to predict `nox` using a first, second, and third degree polynomial in `dis`. The first degree polynomial is just simple linear regression and the regression curve plot will be a straight line as shown in Figure 5-11.

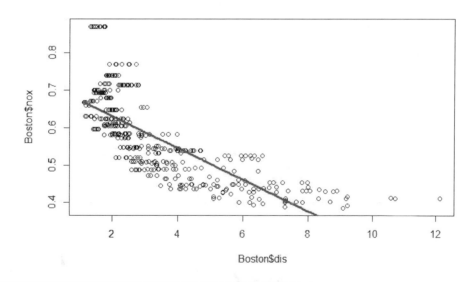

Figure 5-11 Polynomial regression curve of degree 1 – linear fit

There is a pronounced relationship between `nox` and `dis`, but it seems clear that this relationship is non-linear; the data suggest a curved relationship.

```
> library(MASS)
```

```
> data(Boston)
> names(Boston)
> fit_d1 <- lm(nox ~ dis, data=Boston)
> summary(fit_d1)
Call:
  lm(formula = nox ~ dis, data = Boston)


Residuals:
  Min        1Q     Median        3Q       Max
-0.12239  -0.05212  -0.01257   0.04391   0.23041


Coefficients:
                Estimate Std. Error t value Pr(>|t|)
(Intercept)     0.715343   0.006796  105.26   <2e-16 ***
  dis          -0.042331   0.001566  -27.03   <2e-16 ***

  ---
  Signif. codes:  0 '***' 0.001 '**' 0.01 '*' 0.05 '.' 0.1 ' ' 1
Residual standard error: 0.07412 on 504 degrees of freedom
Multiple R-squared:  0.5917,  Adjusted R-squared:  0.5909
F-statistic: 730.4 on 1 and 504 DF,  p-value: < 2.2e-16
> plot(Boston$dis, Boston$nox)
> lines(Boston$dis, fit_d1$fitted, col=2, lwd=3)
```

For higher degree regression formulas, we'll use the `poly()` function to come up with the powers of `dis`. Using `poly(dis, 2, raw=TRUE)` yields a matrix with dimension 506 by 2. This yields the quadratic form of polynomial. The `raw=TRUE` tells the function to use raw and not orthogonal polynomials.

Another way to create the polynomial basis function is to use the `I()` wrapper function in R as in `dis + I(dis^2)` to get an equivalent polynomial. The `I()` function is necessary because the caret used inside a formula does not have its usual mathematical meaning—to raise to a power. In either case, we produce a non-linear fit. The familiar non-linear quadratic shaped curve is shown in Figure 5-12.

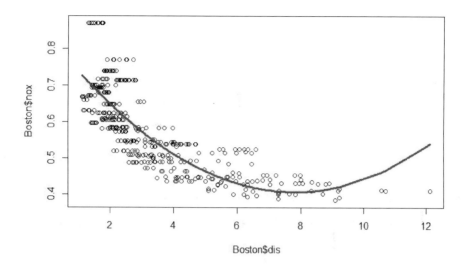

Figure 5-12 Polynomial regression curve of degree 2 – quadratic fit

Note that the quadratic fit appears to be better than the fit obtained when just the linear term is included. Also note the R^2 of the quadratic fit is 0.6999, compared to 0.5917 for the linear fit.

```
> fit_d2 <- lm(nox ~ poly(dis, 2, raw=TRUE), data=Boston)
> summary(fit_d2)
Call:
 lm(formula = nox ~ poly(dis, 2, raw = TRUE), data = Boston)
Residuals:
      Min        1Q     Median        3Q        Max
-0.129559 -0.044514 -0.007753  0.025778  0.201882


Coefficients:
                            Estimate Std. Error t value Pr(>|t|)
(Intercept)                 0.843991   0.011196   75.39   <2e-16 ***
 poly(dis, 2, raw = TRUE)1 -0.111628   0.005320  -20.98   <2e-16 ***
 poly(dis, 2, raw = TRUE)2  0.007135   0.000530   13.46   <2e-16 ***
 ---
 Signif. codes:  0 '***' 0.001 '**' 0.01 '*' 0.05 '.' 0.1 ' ' 1
Residual standard error: 0.06361 on 503 degrees of freedom
Multiple R-squared:  0.6999,  Adjusted R-squared:  0.6987
```

```
F-statistic: 586.4 on 2 and 503 DF,  p-value: < 2.2e-16
> plot(Boston$dis, Boston$nox)
> lines(sort(Boston$dis), fit_d2$fitted.values[order(Boston$dis)],
    col = 2, lwd = 3)
```

Now let's fit a linear model using a third degree polynomial. As is said, a picture is worth a thousand words, and so a plot of the non-linear curve that represents the fitted polynomial overlaid on the data is a powerful way of assessing the quality of the fit. Figure 5-13 shows a good fit, but let's look at the statistical values returned by lm() for each degree of polynomial.

- The coefficient of determination (also referred to as the R^2 or R-squared value) for the fit indicates the percent of the variation in the data that is explained by the model. The closer that R^2 is to 1, the more completely the fitted model "explains" the data. Notice how the Adjusted R-squared value increases with the degree of the polynomial: 0.5909, 0.6987, and 0.7131.

- The observed F-statistic for the fit compares the "size" of the fraction of the data variation explained by the model to the size of the variation unexplained by the model. The basis for this comparison is the ratio of the variances for the model and the error (residuals). "Large" values of this F-statistic, typically > 6, indicate that the fit is significant.

- The observed t-statistics (also known as "t value") for the coefficients indicate the level of significance for any one of the coefficients. The t-statistic is defined as the ratio of the value of the coefficient to its standard error. A coefficient is usually significant if its t-value is 2 or better.

```
> fit_d3 <- lm(nox ~ poly(dis, 3, raw=TRUE), data=Boston)
> summary(fit_d3)
> coef(summary(fit_d3))
Call:
  lm(formula = nox ~ poly(dis, 3, raw = TRUE), data = Boston)


Residuals:
     Min       1Q    Median       3Q       Max
```

```
-0.121130 -0.040619 -0.009738  0.023385  0.194904


Coefficients:
                               Estimate Std. Error t value Pr(>|t|)
(Intercept)                   0.9341281  0.0207076  45.110  < 2e-16 ***
  poly(dis, 3, raw = TRUE)1  -0.1820817  0.0146973 -12.389  < 2e-16 ***
  poly(dis, 3, raw = TRUE)2   0.0219277  0.0029329   7.476 3.43e-13 ***
  poly(dis, 3, raw = TRUE)3  -0.0008850  0.0001727  -5.124 4.27e-07 ***
  ---
  Signif. codes:  0 '***' 0.001 '**' 0.01 '*' 0.05 '.' 0.1 ' ' 1


Residual standard error: 0.06207 on 502 degrees of freedom
Multiple R-squared:  0.7148,  Adjusted R-squared:  0.7131
F-statistic: 419.3 on 3 and 502 DF,  p-value: < 2.2e-16


> plot(Boston$dis, Boston$nox)
> lines(sort(Boston$dis), fit_d3$fitted.values[order(Boston$dis)],
    col = 2, lwd = 3)
```

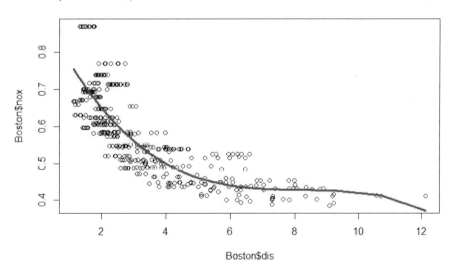

Figure 5-13 Polynomial regression curve of degree 3 – qubic fit

We can see that including higher order terms to the formula led to improvement in the model, so why not keep adding more terms of higher degrees? The resulting fit for higher degrees may result in curves that are too wavy, i.e., it is unclear that including the additional terms will lead to a better fit to the data.

When using polynomial regression, we must determine which degree of the polynomial to use. Aside from the statistics rules listed above, we can use hypothesis tests. In our example, we have fit models ranging from linear to third degree polynomials and seek to decide the simplest model that is sufficient to explain the relationship between nox and dis. We can use the anova() function to perform a hypothesis test comparing the three models. *Analysis of variance* is used to test the null hypothesis that model M_1 is sufficient to explain the data against the alternative hypothesis that a more complex model M_2 is required. In the call to anova(), we'll pass model arguments in increasing complexity: fit_d1, fit_d2, and fit_d3. The resulting ANOVA table shows how the different models compare. The p-values are useful here. We read down the list of values in the Pr(>F) column. In the second row, for Model 2, we do <u>not</u> accept the null hypothesis "there wasn't a significant improvement of the model" by adding another term to the polynomial if the p-value is greater than 0.05. In this case, the value is very small, 2.2e-16, meaning there was improvement. Next, we go down to the third row, for Model 3, and repeat the process. Again, we see there was improvement with a very small p-value, which means the third degree polynomial is the best fit for the non-linear data and will provide the most predictive power.

```
> anova(fit_d1, fit_d2, fit_d3)
Analysis of Variance Table
Model 1: nox ~ dis
Model 2: nox ~ poly(dis, 2, raw = TRUE)
Model 3: nox ~ poly(dis, 3, raw = TRUE)
  Res.Df    RSS Df Sum of Sq        F     Pr(>F)
1    504 2.7686
2    503 2.0353  1   0.73330  190.329 < 2.2e-16 ***
3    502 1.9341  1   0.10116   26.255 4.275e-07 ***
  ---
  Signif. codes:  0 '***' 0.001 '**' 0.01 '*' 0.05 '.' 0.1 ' ' 1
```

SUMMARY

This chapter served as the launching point for carrying out supervised machine learning using regression methods. Regression is the oldest and best understood algorithm and is widely used for a broad spectrum of problem domains. We considered three forms of regression in this chapter: simple linear regression, multiple linear regression, and polynomial regression. In Chapter 6, we'll turn our attention to the various methods of classification. Later, in Chapter 7, we'll explore techniques for evaluating the performance of statistical learning algorithms including regression. This is not the end of the story regarding regression. There are other types of regression such as shrinkage methods like *ridge regression* and the *lasso*, which are designed to reduce variance by shrinking the regression coefficients towards zero. These forms of regression, however, are beyond the scope of this book.

Here is a summary of what you've learned in this chapter:
- We began by exploring simple linear regression using the least squares method of computation provided by R's `lm()` function.
- Using the `summary()` function, we reviewed a number of statistical measures such as the model's fitted values, coefficients, residuals, standard error, t value, p value, and F-statistic.
- We saw that once we trained the model, we could then use it to make predictions with new data.
- We examined a number of important plots to evaluate the quality of the model's fit: residuals vs. fitted values plot, Q-Q plot, Cook's Distance, etc.
- We then saw how the simple linear regression algorithm can be extended to multiple predictors using multiple linear regression. Here, we split the data set into a training set and test set, a common technique used in machine learning.
- We also evaluated the fit of the model using the same methods as with simple linear regression, but we also saw some new diagnostic plots like the Index plot.
- To handle non-linear relationships between the response variable and the predictors, we turned our attention to polynomial regression and explored how different orders of polynomials can improve the quality of the fit.

Chapter 6
Classification

In this chapter we continue exploring the use of machine learning methods for the solution of data science problems. As an extension to Chapter 5, where we studied regression methods, now we'll turn our attention to another very important class of supervised learning: *classification*. In linear regression, we assume that the response variable (what is to be predicted) is quantitative. But in many data science problems, the response variable is qualitative—also known as a categorical variable. For example, gender is qualitative, taking on values of male and female. The process of predicting qualitative responses is called classification.

There are many commonly used classification methods, or classifiers, that a data scientist can use to predict a categorical response variable. In this chapter, we'll significantly expand your machine learning toolbox by discussing the most widely used classification algorithms:

- Logistic regression
- Classification trees
- K-nearest neighbors
- Support vector machines
- Neural networks
- Naïve Bayes
- Random forests
- Gradient boosting trees

As in our discussion of regression in Chapter 5, we will use a training set to build a classifier. Our goal is for the classifier to perform well on the training set and also on the test set containing observations not used to train the classifier.

A SIMPLE EXAMPLE

Let's start off our discussion of classification with a very simple example. We'll examine a data set found in the kernlab package called spam. We can use this data set to build and test a spam classifier algorithm, much like what is found in most e-mail applications these days. The spam data set contains a number of variables representing the frequency with which certain words and punctuation appear in an e-mail. For example, if the words "free," "credit," or "money" appear in the e-mail, then there is a likelihood it is a spam e-mail. The spam data set contains 4601 observations (individual e-mails) with 57 feature variables plus one class label (response variable) type having a value of either "spam" or "nonspam."

In the R code below, we'll look at the frequency of the character "$" (with the charDollar feature variable) and use a density plot for some exploratory data analysis. An e-mail containing "$" is often a condition indicating spam. In Figure 6-1, the x-axis shows the frequency that "$" appeared in the e-mail and the y-axis shows the density, or the number of times a specific frequency appears in the e-mails.

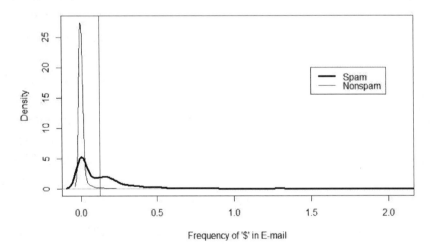

Figure 6-1 **Density plot for spam classifier with boundary for classification purposes**

Most of the e-mails that are spam are represented with a thick line and tend to have more occurrences of the character "$." On the other hand, the non-spam e-mails, the ones we want to receive, have a peak down near zero, meaning fewer have "$" in them. Further, there are few e-mails with a large number of "$" that are non-spam.

```
> plot(density(spam$charDollar[spam$type=="nonspam"]), lwd=0.5,
main="", xlab="Frequency of '$' in E-mail")
> lines(density(spam$charDollar[spam$type=="spam"]), lwd=3)
# > 0.125 -> spam, <= 0.125 -> non-spam
> abline(v=0.125, col="black")
> legend(1.5,20,legend=c("Spam","Nonspam"), lwd=c(3,0.5), lty=1)
```

We can develop a simple algorithm to define a boundary value where if the frequency of "$" is greater than the boundary then we predict spam. Otherwise, we predict non-spam. Let's go back to look at our data through use of the exploratory plot. We choose 0.125 for the frequency boundary value. So above 0.125 the e-mail is spam, and below 0.125 it is non-spam. In the plot we can see the large spike of non-spam e-mails is below 0.125, and that one of the big spikes of the spam e-mails is above the boundary value.

Now we can evaluate the simple classification algorithm to see how well it predicts. To do this we calculate a prediction for each of the e-mails in the spam data set. In the code below, the spam_classifier vector contains either "spam" or "nonspam" for each e-mail in the data set based on the boundary value we chose. Then we make a table of those classifications using the spam_classifier vector and dividing by the total number of observations in the data set. The table can be interpreted like this: When the e-mail is nonspam, we get that classification accuracy of 59.1% of the time and when the e-mail is spam, we get that correct 16.6% of the time. So the total accuracy of the algorithm is 59.1 + 16.6, i.e., 75.7% of the time it is correct. This is how we'd evaluate the accuracy of our simple classifier algorithm even though this is an optimistic estimate of the overall error rate.

```
> spam_classifier <- ifelse(spam$charDollar > 0.125, "spam",
"nonspam")
> table(spam_classifier, spam$type)/nrow(spam)
spam_classifier  nonspam     spam
nonspam          0.5911758  0.2279939
spam             0.0147794  0.1660509
```

LOGISTIC REGRESSION

The first classification algorithm we'll explore is called *logistic regression*. This supervised learning method is essentially applying a transformation of the output of a linear regression such that it fits into a binary response. In other words it mimics the "probability" of a binary output. So rather than modeling the response variable directly, logistic regression models the probability that the response belongs to a particular category. Many problems fit into this representation like the spam problem in the previous section—the binary response is either spam or non-spam, or an online transaction is fraudulent or not, or a tumor is malignant or not. In other words, logistic regression is typically used when there is one binary response variable and a quantitative predictor variable that is related to the probability or odds of the response variable. The algorithm also can be used with categorical variables and with multiple predictors. Logistic regression is often considered the most popular machine learning technique applied in solving classification problems.

As an example, let's use logistic regression on the `iris` data set. We'll try to predict whether an observation is for the "versicolor" species (i.e., is versicolor or is not versicolor). In the code below, we set up the problem by generating a training set `train_iris` and test set `test_iris` for use with the algorithm. We'll use these two data sets throughout this chapter. Since logistic regression utilizes a binary response, we shall create a new column `isVersicolor` for the `iris` data frame. This column contains a `true` or `false` depending on whether the observation is for "versicolor" or not.

```
> data(iris)
> n <- nrow(iris) # Number of observations
> ntrain <- round(n*0.6) # 60% for training set
> set.seed(333)   # Set seed for reproducible results
> tindex <- sample(n, ntrain)  # Create an index
> train_iris <- iris[tindex,]  # Create training set
> test_iris <- iris[-tindex,]  # Create test set
> newcol <-
      data.frame(isVersicolor=(train_iris$Species=="versicolor"))
> train_iris <- cbind(train_iris, newcol)
```

```
> head(train_iris)
    Sepal.Length Sepal.Width Petal.Length Petal.Width  Species      isVersicolor
71  5.9          3.2         4.8          1.8          versicol     TRUE
13  4.8          3.0         1.4          0.1          setosa       FALSE
145 6.7          3.3         5.7          2.5          virginica    FALSE
84  6.0          2.7         5.1          1.6          versicolor   TRUE
3   4.7          3.2         1.3          0.2          setosa       FALSE
105 6.5          3.0         5.8          2.2          virginica    FALSE
```

Now we use the `glm()` function that fits generalized linear models, a class of models that includes logistic regression. `glm()` is part of the `stats` package that is included with base R, so there's no need to install a package. The syntax of `glm()` should be familiar since it is similar to `lm()`. First, we specify the formula to use with the algorithm. In this case, the response variable is the new binary variable `isVersicolor` that we just created. Next, we call `glm()` using a single predictor `Sepal.Width`. In the resulting model table, the first parameter is the intercept and the second is the slope of the graph of `isVersicolor` against `Sepal.Width`. Here, we see that the object `glm1` gets a generalized linear model in which `isVersicolor` is modeled as a function of a single quantitative predictor variable, `Sepal.Width`, using an error distribution from the binomial family.

```
> glm1 <- glm(isVersicolor ~ Sepal.Width, data=train_iris,
      family=binomial)
> summary(glm1)
Call:
  glm(formula = isVersicolor ~ Sepal.Width, family = binomial,
      data = train_iris)
Deviance Residuals:
    Min       1Q   Median       3Q      Max
-1.9933  -0.8609  -0.4757   0.9359   2.1143
Coefficients:
             Estimate Std. Error z value Pr(>|z|)
(Intercept)    9.1013     2.5534   3.564 0.000365 ***
Sepal.Width   -3.3010     0.8656  -3.813 0.000137 ***
```

```
---
Signif. codes:  0 '***' 0.001 '**' 0.01 '*' 0.05 '.' 0.1 ' ' 1
(Dispersion parameter for binomial family taken to be 1)
Null deviance: 113.136  on 89  degrees of freedom
Residual deviance:  90.326  on 88  degrees of freedom
AIC: 94.326
Number of Fisher Scoring iterations: 5
```

It is interesting to see a scatterplot of the response and predictor variables and then to superimpose another curve using the predict() function for the generalized linear model. The plot shown in Figure 6-2 depicts the dichotomist nature of the algorithm. This is called a sigmoid function curve. Notice how the y-axis shows values of isVersicolor between 0 and 1, thus representing probabilities for different values in the training set for Sepal.Width.

```
> plot(train_iris$Sepal.Width, train_iris$isVersicolor)
> curve(predict(glm1, data.frame(Sepal.Width=x), type="response"),
     add=TRUE)
```

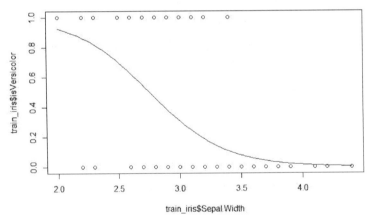

Figure 6-2 Logistic regression plot exhibiting the shape of a sigmoid function

Lastly, we can use the predict() function to determine the classification probability for a single new observation. We'll determine the probability for a Sepal.Width value of 2.4. In this case, the probability is 76.4% that the response variable is species Versicolor.

```
> newdata <- data.frame(Sepal.Width=2.4)
```

```
> predict(glm1, newdata, type="response")
     1
0.7647645
```

Next, we can use multiple predictors with logistic regression. The predictors will be the four quantitative variables in the data set. In the call to `glm()`, we pass the formula, the training set, and as before the argument `family=binomial` in order to tell R to run a logistic regression (there are other types of generalized linear models available) and create the `glm2` object.

We can then use `summary(glm2)` to investigate the results of the algorithm. The model table looks just as it would for a multiple regression. We see the smallest p-value is associated with `Sepal.Width`, meaning there is an association between `Sepal.Width` and `isVersicolor`. We also can use the `coef()` function in order to access the coefficients for this fitted model and the `summary()` function to access components of the fitted model such as p-values for the coefficients.

```
> formula <- isVersicolor ~Sepal.Length + Sepal.Width +
      Petal.Length + Petal.Width
> glm2 <- glm(formula, data=train_iris, family="binomial")
> summary(glm2)
Call:
  glm(formula = formula, family = "binomial", data = train_iris)
Deviance Residuals:
   Min       1Q    Median       3Q      Max
-2.0732  -0.7529  -0.4250   0.9386   2.2185
Coefficients:
                Estimate Std. Error z value Pr(>|z|)
(Intercept)      5.9490     3.3423    1.780   0.07509 .
Sepal.Length     0.4966     0.8340    0.595   0.55156
Sepal.Width     -3.2680     1.0456   -3.125   0.00178 **
Petal.Length     0.5930     0.7837    0.757   0.44920
Petal.Width     -1.7861     1.3396   -1.333   0.18241

---
```

```
 Signif. codes:  0 '***' 0.001 '**' 0.01 '*' 0.05 '.' 0.1 ' ' 1
(Dispersion parameter for binomial family taken to be 1)
    Null deviance: 113.136  on 89  degrees of freedom
Residual deviance:  87.066  on 85  degrees of freedom
AIC: 97.066
Number of Fisher Scoring iterations: 5
> coef(glm2)
(Intercept) Sepal.Length  Sepal.Width Petal.Length  Petal.Width
  5.9489966    0.4966006   -3.2679800    0.5930357   -1.7861451
> summary(glm2)$coef
               Estimate Std. Error    z value    Pr(>|z|)
(Intercept)   5.9489966  3.3422812  1.7799211 0.075088880
Sepal.Length  0.4966006  0.8340266  0.5954254 0.551559180
Sepal.Width  -3.2679800  1.0456208 -3.1253970 0.001775653
Petal.Length  0.5930357  0.7836647  0.7567467 0.449201602
Petal.Width  -1.7861451  1.3395827 -1.3333593 0.182413915
```

Once the glm2 model has been successfully trained, we can use the predict() function to make predictions for the test set. The type="response" argument tells R to output probabilities that the response is 1 given the predictors.

```
> prob <- predict(glm2, newdata=test_iris, type="response")
> round(prob,3)
1     5     6     8     9     11    14    15    19    20    21
0.077 0.054 0.021 0.105 0.295 0.051 0.223 0.020 0.040 0.027 0.138
23    29    31    36    39    41    45    46    49    51    57
0.036 0.108 0.230 0.158 0.222 0.059 0.029 0.236 0.048 0.322 0.145
58    60    64    65    67    68    69    73    74    75    78
0.670 0.382 0.447 0.282 0.253 0.657 0.862 0.757 0.616 0.470 0.355
79    81    82    85    94    96    97    99    106   107   109
0.364 0.755 0.776 0.234 0.748 0.337 0.371 0.531 0.521 0.461 0.791
111   114   116   119   125   127   129   131   133   134   137
0.138 0.501 0.092 0.779 0.133 0.380 0.389 0.668 0.347 0.568 0.047
```

```
141    144    147    149    150
0.139 0.149 0.618 0.048 0.247
```

CLASSIFICATION TREES

Next, we'll consider classification trees and how to apply this machine learning method to typical classification problems, specifically to predict a qualitative response. Classification trees are considered non-linear models. All tree-based techniques produce one or more tree objects that represent a series of splits from the "root" or top of the tree. In one popular implementation (from the tree package in R), each split is based on finding the one predictor variable (and a given threshold of that variable) that results in the greatest change in explained deviance. Tree methods do this using an exhaustive search of all possible threshold values for each predictor. Once a split is made, the process is repeated for each group separately until all deviance (or some low threshold) is explained or there are too few samples in the remaining subset. We can summarize the tree algorithm in the following way:

1. Consider all the predictors together in one big group.

2. Find the first predictor that best splits the responses into two different homogeneous groups.

3. Divide the data into two groups called "leaves." The split performed is called a "node."

4. Within each split we search through all the predictors again, including the predictor we just split on, and try to find within that group another predictor or split that separates the responses into even more homogeneous groups.

5. Continue the process until the groups are small or sufficiently pure (i.e. homogeneous) enough to halt the algorithm

In order to understand classification trees, we can use the tree library to analyze the iris data set. Bear in mind, there are a number of other tree packages in R, such as the rpart and party packages, but in this section we'll use tree, which is easier to use because it is based on familiar deviance statistics. In the `iris` data set, `Species` is the categorical response variable, and the other continuous variables are the predictors. First, we need to install and load the `tree` library.

```
> install.packages("tree")
> library(tree)
```

Let's do some quick EDA to familiarize ourselves with the training set. We see there are 90 observations of five variables, and we can get a feeling for the four predictors and the response.

```
> str(train_iris)
'data.frame':  90 obs. of  5 variables:
 $ Sepal.Length: num  5.9 4.8 6.7 6 4.7 6.5 6.3 5 4.9 5.8 ...
 $ Sepal.Width : num  3.2 3 3.3 2.7 3.2 3 2.3 3.5 3.1 2.7 ...
 $ Petal.Length: num  4.8 1.4 5.7 5.1 1.3 5.8 4.4 1.6 1.5 5.1 ...
 $ Petal.Width : num  1.8 0.1 2.5 1.6 0.2 2.2 1.3 0.6 0.1 1.9 ...
 $ Species     : Factor w/ 3 levels "setosa","versicolor",..: 2 1 3 2
    1 3 2 1 1 3 ...
```

Next, we will train the classification tree algorithm using the training data set `train_iris` in order to predict `Species`. Notice `Species` is specified as the response variable and the rest of the variables in the data set serve as predictors using the notation `Species~`. when calling the `tree()` function. The syntax of the `tree()` function is similar to that of the `lm()` function. The classification tree object is returned in `ct1`.

```
> ct1 <- tree(Species~., data=train_iris)
```

One of the reasons why decision trees are so popular in machine learning is because they're very visual and can be easily interpreted. As evidence of this, let's proceed to plot the tree structure using the `plot()` function and the `text()` function to display the node labels as shown in Figure 6-3. This type of visualization is often referred to as a *dendrogram*. Following the splits in the tree, we can see that if `Petal.Length < 2.7`, then the species is always `setosa` in the training set.

```
> plot(ct1)
> text(ct1)
```

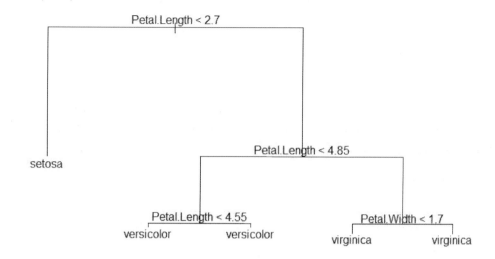

Figure 6-3 Classification tree for the iris data set predicting Species

Printing the classification tree object `ct1` as shown below provides information about the threshold of each split, the node sample size, the associated residual deviance, and the predicted value. You also get the fraction of presences and absences (i.e., the frequency of each response class) for the samples of each node. For example, in the results below there is a split that says `Petal.Length < 2.7` where all 30 of the observations where this condition is true have species `setosa`.

```
> ct1
node), split, n, deviance, yval, (yprob)
* denotes terminal node
1) root 90 197.700 virginica ( 0.33333 0.32222 0.34444 )
2) Petal.Length < 2.7 30    0.000 setosa ( 1.00000 0.00000 0.00000 )
     *
  3) Petal.Length > 2.7 60   83.110 virginica ( 0.00000 0.48333
     0.51667 )
6) Petal.Length < 4.85 28    8.628 versicolor ( 0.00000 0.96429
     0.03571 )
12) Petal.Length < 4.55 21    0.000 versicolor ( 0.00000 1.00000
     0.00000 ) *
```

```
 13) Petal.Length > 4.55 7   5.742 versicolor ( 0.00000 0.85714
     0.14286 ) *
  7) Petal.Length > 4.85 32  14.960 virginica ( 0.00000 0.06250
     0.93750 )
14) Petal.Width < 1.7 5   6.730 virginica ( 0.00000 0.40000 0.60000
    ) *
 15) Petal.Width > 1.7 27   0.000 virginica ( 0.00000 0.00000
     1.00000 ) *
```

We can use the `summary()` function to list the variables that are used as internal nodes in the tree, the number of terminal nodes, and the training error rate. We learn that only two variables are used to predict species (`Petal.Length` and `Petal.Width`), and that only 3% of the predicted values are misclassified in this model.

```
> summary(ct1)
Classification tree:
 tree(formula = Species ~ ., data = train_iris)
Variables actually used in tree construction:
 [1] "Petal.Length" "Petal.Width"
Number of terminal nodes: 5
Residual mean deviance: 0.1467 = 12.47 / 85
Misclassification error rate: 0.03333 = 3 / 90
```

Now we can see how well the trained classification tree performs on the test set. Once again, we apply the `prediction()` function. In the code below, we calculate a vector of predicted class labels from the fitted tree object. Here, `prediction` contains predicted values of the response `Species` for the observations in `test_iris`.

```
> prediction <- predict(ct1, newdata=test_iris, type='class')
> prediction
 [1] setosa     setosa     setosa     setosa     setosa     setosa
 [7] setosa     setosa     setosa     setosa     setosa     setosa
[13] setosa     setosa     setosa     setosa     setosa     setosa
[19] setosa     setosa     versicolor versicolor versicolor versicolor
[25] versicolor versicolor versicolor versicolor versicolor virginica
```

```
[31] versicolor versicolor virginica   versicolor versicolor versicolor
[37] versicolor versicolor versicolor  versicolor versicolor virginica
[43] versicolor virginica   virginica   virginica   virginica   virginica
[49] virginica   versicolor virginica   virginica   virginica   virginica
[55] virginica   virginica   virginica   virginica   virginica   virginica
Levels: setosa versicolor virginica
```

Finally, we can use `table()` to show a confusion matrix to see how accurate tree has predicted the response. We see that 93% of the test observations are correctly classified. Remember the test set only has 60 observations out of the 150 observations in the `iris` data set.

```
> table(prediction, test_iris$Species)
prediction  setosa versicolor virginica
setosa        20      0          0
versicolor    0       19         2
virginica     0       2          17
> (20+19+17)/60
[1] 0.9333333
```

NAÏVE BAYES

Next, we'll turn to the naïve Bayes classifier, another popular supervised machine learning algorithm. This learning method is based on conditional probability, or the likelihood of observing one thing given some other thing that's already known. Naïve Bayes applies Bayes' theorem (from Bayesian statistics) with strong (naive) independence assumptions. Despite its simplicity, Naive Bayes can often outperform more sophisticated classification methods.

In simple terms, a Naïve Bayes classifier assumes that the presence (or absence) of a particular feature of a class is unrelated to the presence (or absence) of any other feature. For example, an animal may be considered to be a dog if it has a coat of fur, four legs, tail, and also barks. Even if these features depend on each other or upon the existence of the other features, a

Naïve Bayes classifier considers all of these properties to independently contribute to the probability that this animal is a dog.

An advantage of the Naïve Bayes classifier is that it only requires a small amount of training data to estimate the parameters (means and variances of the variables) necessary for classification. Because independent variables are assumed, only the variances of the variables for each class need to be determined and not the entire covariance matrix.

The advantages of Naïve Bayes are that it is:

- Not sensitive to irrelevant features
- Fast to train with a single scan
- Fast to classify
- Able to handle an arbitrary number of predictors either continuous or categorical
- Able to handle streaming data well
- Particularly suited with high dimensionality

The disadvantage of Naïve Bayes is that it:

- Assumes independence of features

To illustrate Naïve Bayes, we'll use the `naiveBayes()` function in the `e1071` package. `e1071` is a treasure trove of machine learning algorithms, and we'll also use this package to support vector machines later in this chapter. For this example, we'll use the `iris` data set. `naiveBayes()` computes the conditional a-posterior probabilities of a categorical class variable given independent predictor variables using the Bayes rule.

Now we can start our example by installing and loading the `e1071` package. Next, we'll call the `naiveBayes()` algorithm using `Species` as the response variable and the other variables as the predictors. We'll use the `iris` training data set `train_iris` for this purpose. Once the Naïve Bayes object `nb1` is created, we can display its contents to better understand what the algorithm provides. An object like `nb1` of class `naiveBayes` includes two components: `apriori`, containing a class distribution for the dependent variable, and `tables`, a list of tables with one for each predictor variable. For a continuous variable there is a table for each target class that gives the mean and standard deviation of the variable. As we'll see below, we can easily reference the object's constituent parts.

```
> install.packages("e1071")
> library(e1071)
> nb1 <-naiveBayes(Species~., data=train_iris)
> nb1
Naive Bayes Classifier for Discrete Predictors
Call:
  naiveBayes.default(x = X, y = Y, laplace = laplace)
A-priori probabilities:
Y
   setosa versicolor  virginica
0.3333333  0.3222222  0.3444444


Conditional probabilities:
             Sepal.Length
Y                  [,1]       [,2]
  setosa       4.983333 0.3141308
  versicolor   6.024138 0.4740819
  virginica    6.654839 0.6297294


             Sepal.Width
Y                  [,1]       [,2]
  setosa       3.403333 0.4089375
  versicolor   2.779310 0.3244548
  virginica    3.009677 0.3279785


             Petal.Length
Y                  [,1]       [,2]
  setosa       1.480000 0.1349329
  versicolor   4.306897 0.3890749
  virginica    5.577419 0.5321088
```

```
          Petal.Width
Y                   [,1]       [,2]
  setosa      0.2533333 0.1224276
  versicolor 1.3379310 0.1859604
  virginica  2.0129032 0.2883770
```

Now let's use the `predict()` function on the test set to make predictions using the Naïve Bayes model we just trained. To test its accuracy, we can display a confusion matrix using the `table()` function with the predicted and actual response values as arguments. The resulting table for our example shows that the prediction is quite accurate since there are only three observations that were misclassified. We can quickly come up with an accuracy metric by summing up the total number of accurate classifications (the number along the diagonal in the matrix) and dividing by the number of observations. We get 95%, which is very good.

This example shows that a Naïve Bayes classifier makes few mistakes in a dataset that, although simple, is not linearly separable as shown in the confusion matrix, where all misclassifications are between versicolor and virginica species.

```
> prediction <- predict(nb1, test_iris[,-5])
> xtab <- table(prediction, test_iris$Species)
> xtab
prediction   setosa versicolor virginica
  setosa          20          0         0
  versicolor       0         20         2
  virginica        0          1        17
```

To see what's going on under the hood in the nb1 object, let's use the following command, which gives the class distributions in the data - the prior distribution of the classes ("A priori" is Latin for "from before"):

```
> nb1$apriori
Y
  setosa versicolor virginica
    30      29          31
```

Since the predictor variables here are all continuous, the Naïve Bayes classifier generates three Gaussian (Normal) distributions for each predictor variable: one for each value of the class variable `Species`. If you use the command below, you will see the mean (first column) and standard deviation (second column) for the three class-dependent Gaussian distributions.

```
> nb1$tables$Petal.Length
              Petal.Length
Y                 [,1]        [,2]
   setosa     1.480000  0.1349329
   versicolor 4.306897  0.3890749
   virginica  5.577419  0.5321088
```

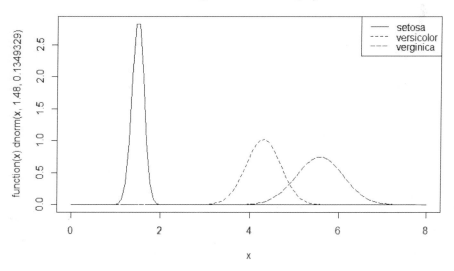

Figure 6-4 Petal length distribution by species

By plugging in the values from the above table, we can plot these three distributions against each other with the following R commands as shown in Figure 6-4. Notice that the `setosa` species (the smooth curve) tends to have smaller petals (mean value = 1.48) and less variation in petal length (standard deviation is only 0.1349329).

```
> plot(function(x) dnorm(x, 1.48, 0.1349329), 0, 8, lty=1,
    main="Petal length distribution by species")
> curve(dnorm(x, 4.306897, 0.3890749), add=TRUE, lty=2)
> curve(dnorm(x, 5.577419, 0.5321088 ), add=TRUE, lty=5)
> legend('topright', legend=c("setosa", "versicolor", "verginica"),
    lty=c(1,2,5), bty='o')
```

K-NEAREST NEIGHBORS

The K-nearest neighbors (KNN) classifier is another commonly used supervised machine learning algorithm. It is arguably the most straightforward algorithm in this book. As a simple example, consider a "mental algorithm" using similarity data to recommend a new food to a friend based on the kind of food she already enjoys. This intuition is basically a 1-nearest neighbors algorithm. A K-nearest neighbors algorithm, continuing with this theme, is a generalization of this intuition where you draw on more than one data point before making a recommendation. In the food selection example, the K-nearest neighbors algorithm is like asking your friends for a recommendation. We begin with asking people with whom we share similar taste and then asking them for recommendations. If a majority of them recommend the same food, we conclude that we'll like it too.

The purpose of the KNN algorithm is to use a data set in which the data points are separated into several separate classes to predict the classification of a new sample point. KNN is often used when we don't know the conditional distribution of the response given the predictor(s), which makes using the Bayes classifier for predicting qualitative responses impossible. Many approaches attempt to estimate the conditional distribution of the response given predictor(s) and then classify a given observation to the class with highest estimated probability. KNN is one such method.

To illustrate KNN, we'll use the knn() function in the class package. KNN is also called *instance based learning*, in contrast to *model based learning*, because it is not learning any model in a real sense. The training process is essentially memorizing all the training data.

The strength of KNN is found in its simplicity since no model needs to be trained. Unlike other model-fitting algorithms that we have encountered thus far, rather than a two-step process in which we first fit the model and then use the model to make predictions, KNN forms predictions using a single function call. Incremental learning is automatic when more data arrives. Old data can be removed as well. The weakness of KNN is that it doesn't handle high dimensionality well.

In order to visualize how KNN works, let's take a simple example using the `iris` data set. Specifically, we'll use a scatterplot in two-dimensional space consisting of two predictors, `PetalWidth` and `PetalLength`, for observations in the training set we've been using. The R code below produces Figure 6-5, which shows a plot with the different values of the response variable `Species` denoted with different symbols.

```
> plot(train_iris$Petal.Length, train_iris$Petal.Width,
     pch=c(train_iris$Species))
> legend('topleft', legend=c("setosa", "versicolor", "verginica"),
     pch=c(1,2,3), bty='o')
```

In order to determine the *nearest neighbors*, we need a distance function to be defined as measuring the distance from one data point to another. Euclidean distance is a common metric used for numeric variables when determining "nearness." To predict a new data point, denoted with the "?" character in the plot, we determine the closest K (a tuning argument that is a positive integer) neighbors from the training set and let them vote for the final prediction. In this example, we'll use K=5 so the five nearest observations are 3 `versicolor` and 2 `virginica`; as a result, the new data point is classified by KNN as `versicolor` based on the vote of the five nearest neighbors.

The KNN algorithm proceeds for each row of the test set, finding the K nearest training set vectors with the classification decided by majority vote with ties broken at random. If there are ties for the Kth nearest vector, all candidates are included in the vote. The voting can also be weighted among the K neighbors based on their distance from the new data point.

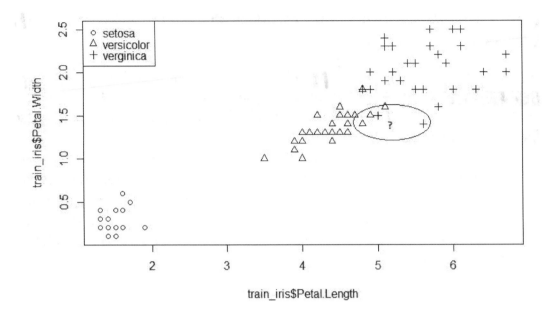

Figure 6-5 Finding nearest neighbors with K=5

As an important side note, since the KNN classifier predicts the class of a given test observation by identifying the observations that are nearest to it, the scale of the variables matters. Any values of variables that are large will have a much larger effect on the distance between the observations and smaller valued variables will have a smaller effect. For example, as far as KNN is concerned, a difference in $10,000 in home price is enormous compared to a number of rooms difference of 2. A good way to manage this problem is to standardize the data so that all variables are given a mean of zero and a standard deviation of one. Then all the variables will be on a comparable scale. See the "Feature Scaling" section of Chapter 3 for more details on using the `scale()` function.

Here are some characteristics of the KNN algorithm to remember:

- Choose an odd K value for a two-class problem.

- K must not be a multiple of the number of classes.

- The main drawback of KNN is the complexity in searching the nearest neighbors for each sample. This means the algorithm exhibits a certain level of CPU and memory greediness.

- KNN has an insensitivity to outliers that makes it resilient to any errors in the classification data.

Let's look at how KNN is used for prediction with an example using the `iris` data set. First, we'll install and load the `class` library, a package containing functions for classification. Next, we'll divide the training set `train_iris` into two pieces consisting of predictors and response and then do the same to the test set `test_iris`. The `knn()` function requires data frames containing the training set predictors as the first argument, the test set predictors as its second argument, and the training set response values as its third argument. The fourth argument is K, which controls the KNN algorithm as discussed above. The result is a factor variable, in this case `prediction`, containing classifications of the test set.

```
> install.packages("class")
> library(class)
> train_x <- train_iris[,-5] # Training set predictors
> train_y <- train_iris[,5]  # Training set response
> test_x <- test_iris[,-5]   # Test set predictors
> test_y <- test_iris[,5]    # Test set response
> prediction <- knn(train_x, test_x, train_y, k=5)
```

In order to test the accuracy of KNN, we can display a confusion matrix using the `table()` function with the predicted and actual response values as arguments. The resulting table for our example shows that the prediction is quite accurate since there is only one observation that was misclassified. We can quickly come up with an accuracy metric by summing up the total number of accurate classification and divide by the number of observations. We get 98.3%, which is very good.

```
> table(prediction, test_iris$Species)
prediction   setosa versicolor virginica
  setosa         20          0         0
  versicolor      0         21         1
  virginica       0          0        18
```

```
(20+21+18)/nrow(test_iris)
[1] 0.9833333
sum(prediction != test_y)   # Number of misclassifications
[1] 1
length(test_y)    # Number of observations
[1] 60
```

SUPPORT VECTOR MACHINES

The next classification algorithm we'll discuss is called the *Support Vector Machine* (SVM). SVMs have become quite popular in the data science community and tend to perform well in a variety of problem domains. A true understanding of the SVM algorithm requires a thorough comprehension of the mathematical basis for this statistical learning technique. This motivation, however, is beyond the scope of this book, so as an alternative we will provide a non-mathematical perspective of the SVM to introduce the subject.

A SVM is primarily a classier method that performs classification tasks by constructing hyperplanes in a multidimensional space that separates cases of different class labels. You can use a SVM when your data has exactly two classes, e.g., binary classification problems (although extensions to the model are able to handle the case of more than two classes). A SVM classifies data by finding the best *hyperplane* that separates all data points of one class from those of the other class; in other words, it separates observations according to their class labels. The idea is to accommodate classes separable by a linear boundary as well as non-linear class boundaries. The *best* hyperplane for a SVM means the one with the largest *margin* between the two classes. Margin means the maximal width of the slice parallel to the hyperplane that has no interior data points. The *support vectors* are the data points that are closest to the separating hyperplane; these points are on the boundary of the slice. They *support* the maximal margin hyperplane in the sense that if these points were moved slightly, then the hyperplane would move as well.

Figure 6-6 illustrates these definitions using an example of a linear classifier having two feature variables where a solid circle indicates data points of one class and a hollow circle indicates data points of the other class. In this two-dimensional case, the separating hyperplane is just a line. In three dimensions, the separating hyperplane would be an ordinary plane. Here, the data are linearly separable since we can see there are many possible lines that separate the classes.

Most classification problems are not that simple, and often more complex decision boundary structures are needed in order to make an optimal separation, i.e., correctly classify new objects (in the test set) on the basis of the observations that are available (in the training set). Classification problems based on drawing separating lines to distinguish between objects of different class memberships are known as hyperplane classifiers. If the data distribution is fundamentally non-linear, the trick is to transform the data to a higher dimension where, hopefully, the data are linearly separable. In this case, the original data points of one class are mapped (i.e., rearranged) using a set of mathematical functions known as *kernels*. The process of rearranging the data points is known as mapping (transformation). Note that in this new setting, the mapped data points are linearly separable, and thus instead of constructing the complex curve, all we have to do is to find an optimal line that can separate the classes.

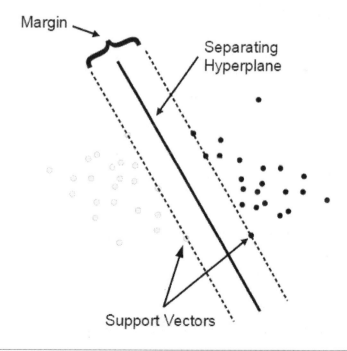

Figure 6-6 Conceptual diagram for a support vector machine in two dimensions

(http://www.di.fc.ul.pt/~jpn/r/svm/svm.html)

In order to demonstrate the SVM algorithm, we'll use the `svm()` function found in the `e1071` package on the `iris` data set. The code below trains a model using the `train_iris` training set. A number of arguments are passed to `svm()` including the formula `Species~.` which says we want to classify the `Species` response variable using all the other predictors found in the data set, `Sepal.Length`, `Sepal.Width`, `Petal.Length`, and `Petal.Width`. We can also specify the type of usage we'd like for `svm()`. The default is `type="C-classification"` for a classification machine, but `svm()` also can be used as a regression machine. The `kernel` argument has a variety of possible types including linear, polynomial, radial, and sigmoid. We use `kernel="radial"` (the default) for this multi-class classification problem. You can tune the operation of the SVM with two additional arguments: `gamma` and `cost`, where `gamma` is the argument for use by the kernel function and `cost` allows us to specify the cost of a violation to the margin. Thus when the cost is small, the margins will be wide and there will be many support vectors. You will typically experiment with different values of `gamma` and `cost` to find the best classification accuracy.

```
> library(e1071)
> svm1 <- svm(Species~., data=train_iris, method="C-classification",
     kernal="radial", gamma=0.1, cost=10)
```

The `summary()` function shown below provides some useful information regarding how the model was trained. We see that the algorithm discovered 22 support vectors distributed in this way: 10 for the `setosa` class, 3 for the `versicolor` class, and 9 for the `virginica` class.

```
> summary(svm1)
Call:
  svm(formula = Species ~ ., data = train_iris, type = "C-
     classification",
    kernal = "radial", gamma = 0.1, cost = 10)
Parameters:
 SVM-Type: C-classification
 SVM-Kernel: radial
```

```
cost: 10
gamma: 0.1
Number of Support Vectors: 22
( 10 3 9 )
Number of Classes: 3
Levels:
 setosa versicolor virginica
```

You can also display the support vectors calculated by the algorithm using `svm1$SV` value of the fitted model. The display includes the index of the observation in the data set and coefficients of the predictors for the support vectors (location in the original scaled space). I've only included the first five support vectors below instead of all 22 that were found.

```
> svm1$SV    #Show support vectors
     Sepal.Length Sepal.Width Petal.Length Petal.Width
71   0.006532661  0.30579724    0.5624153   0.7747208
84   0.124120557 -0.84094241    0.7315157   0.5125972
88   0.476884245 -1.75833413    0.3369481   0.1194119
86   0.124120557  0.76449310    0.3933149   0.5125972
53   1.182411621  0.07644931    0.6187821   0.3815354
```

There is also a special `plot()` function for SVMs. The idea is to visualize the support vectors (denoted with "x"), the decision boundary, and the margin for the model. Figure 6-7 shows the plot for fitted model using the R code below. The plot helps us visualize a two-dimensional projection of the data (using the `Petal.Width` and `Petal.Length` predictors) with highlighting classes and support vectors. The `Species` classes are shown in different shadings. The `slice` argument is used to specify a list of named values for the dimensions held constant (only needed if more than two variables are used).

```
> plot(svm1, train_iris, Petal.Width ~ Petal.Length,
    slice=list(Sepal.Width=3, Sepal.Length=4))
```

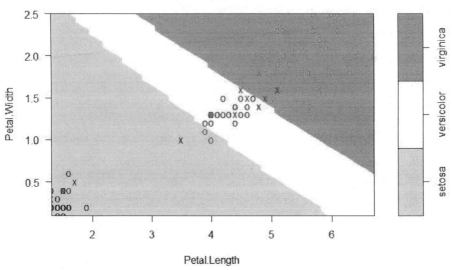

Figure 6-7 SVM plot showing the model's support vectors, decision boundary and margin

Next, we'll use the trained SVM model and the `predict()` function to make predictions using the test set `test_iris`. The result is a factor variable `prediction` containing the predicted classes for each observation in the test set. Then we can create a confusion matrix with the `table()` function to check the accuracy of the model. We can visually inspect the matrix to see there was only one misclassification.

```
> prediction <- predict(svm1, test_iris)
> xtab <- table(test_iris$Species, prediction)
> xtab
          prediction
           setosa versicolor virginica
setosa        20         0         0
versicolor     0        20         1
virginica      0         0        19
```

As we did in the previous section for the KNN classifier, we can check the accuracy of the algorithm with the following R code. The first metric shows how well the trained algorithm makes predictions using the test set. The accuracy of 98.3% is very good. Next we can report the number of misclassifications; in this case, only one observation in the test set was incorrectly classified.

```
> (20+20+19)/nrow(test_iris) # Prediction accuracy
[1] 0.9833333
> sum(prediction != test_y) # Number of misclassifications
[1] 1
```

NEURAL NETWORKS

In this section we will review the *neural network* machine learning algorithm (more formally known as an *artificial neural network*). The concept of a neural network is actually somewhat of an old idea that had fallen out of favor for a period, but today it is considered a state-of-the-art technique for many types of machine learning problems. But why do we need yet another algorithm? The motivation for neural networks is the need for powerful nonlinear models. For example, you might have a non-linear classification problem to solve, and if you tried to use logistic regression, you might get a solution if you only had a couple of feature variables. Logistic regression, however, is not a good way to learn complex nonlinear models. Neural networks are much better, especially when the number of feature variables is large. The use of neural networks is a popular machine learning technique for computer vision, a classification algorithm that examines an image and tells us whether it contains a picture of a particular object.

Neural networks were originally motivated by the goal of machines to mimic the most amazing learning machine we know: the human brain. The brain consists of closely interconnected sets of neurons. Although a particular neuron may be relatively simple in structure, dense networks of interconnected neurons can perform complex learning tasks such as classification. The brain contains around 10^{11} neurons, each connected on average to 10,000 other neurons for a total of 10^{15} synaptic connections. Neural networks represent an attempt to imitate a very basic type of the nonlinear learning that occurs in the networks of neurons found in nature.

The method was widely used in the 1980s and early 1990s, but for various reasons its popularity diminished in the late 1990s. More recently, neural networks have had a major resurgence. (One of the reasons why their popularity waned is because a neural network is a computationally expensive algorithm) But more recently, computers became fast enough to run large scale neural networks. Since 2006, advanced neural networks have been used to realize methods referred to as deep structured learning or more simply *deep learning*. Such algorithms have been demonstrated to be effective at uncovering underlying structure in data and have been successfully applied to a large variety of problems ranging from image classification to natural language processing and speech recognition.

The motivation for a neural network is depicted in Figure 6-8. This artificial neuron model is used in most neural network algorithms. The inputs are collected from upstream neurons (or the data set) and combined through a combination function, which is then input into a normally nonlinear activation function to produce an output response, and which is then channeled downstream to other neurons.

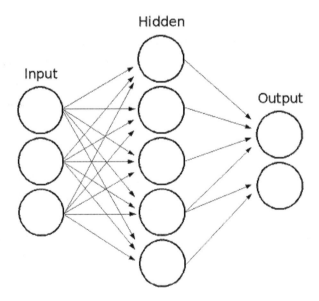

Figure 6-8 Motivation for neural networks
(https://en.wikipedia.org/wiki/Artificial_neural_network)

Neural networks are quite robust with respect to noisy data. Because the network contains many nodes, or artificial neurons, with weights assigned to each connection, the network can learn to work around these information-free or even incorrect examples in the data set. (Unlike decision trees, which produce intuitive rules that are understandable to non-specialists,) neural networks are relatively impervious to human interpretation. In addition, neural networks normally require longer training times than decision trees.

A neural network consists of a network of *artificial neurons* (also called nodes) that are layered, feed forward, and are completely connected. The *feedforward* nature of the network restricts the network to a single direction of flow and does not allow for looping or iteration. The neural network is composed of two or more layers although the typical arrangement (as shown in the figure above) consists of three layers: an *input layer*, a *hidden layer*, and an *output layer*. There may be more than one hidden layer, but one is sufficient for most purposes. The neural network is completely connected in the sense that every neuron in a given layer is connected to every node in the next layer, but not to other neurons in the same layer. Each connection between neurons has a weight associated with it.

The tuning parameters in a neural network include the number of hidden layers and number of neurons in each layer, as well as the learning rate. The number of input nodes normally depends on the number and type of data attributes in the data set. The number of hidden layers and the number of neurons in each hidden layer are both configurable. The number of neurons in the output layer depends on the particular classification task at hand.

One important question when configuring a neural network is determining how many neurons to have in the hidden layer. Since more neurons in the hidden layer increases the power and flexibility of the network for identifying complex patterns, you might be tempted to have a large number of neurons in the hidden layer. This is not, however, always a good strategy since an overly large hidden layer leads to overfitting and jeopardizes the algorithm's ability to generalize with new data. If you see overfitting happening, you can reduce the number of neurons in the hidden layer; conversely, if you find the training accuracy unacceptably low, you should increase the number of neurons in the hidden layer.

The learning in a neural network happens with an iterative feedback mechanism where the error of training data output is used to adjust the corresponding weights on input. This adjustment will be propagated back to previous layers through use of a learning algorithm known as *back propagation.*

In order to demonstrate how we can use neural networks, we'll turn once again to the `iris` data set in order to classify `Species` as the response variable. The code below installs and loads the `neuralnet` package and then makes a copy `nn1_iristrain` of the training set `train_iris` so we can configure the data frame for use by the algorithm.

```
> install.packages("neuralnet")
> library(neuralnet)
> nn1_iristrain <- train_iris
```

The code below essentially creates new binary variables, three per observation, that serve as indicators for whether `Species` has a value equal to one of the species classes: `setosa`, `versicolor`, or `virginica`. We then assign a name to each of the new columns, i.e., Column 6 has the name "setosa," Column 7 has the name "versicolor," and Column 8 has the name "virginica." To visualize the outcome of this code, we use `head()` to see the last four columns of the data frame.

```
> nn1_iristrain <- cbind(nn1_iristrain, train_iris$Species ==
    "setosa")
> nn1_iristrain <- cbind(nn1_iristrain, train_iris$Species ==
    "versicolor")
> nn1_iristrain <- cbind(nn1_iristrain, train_iris$Species ==
    "virginica")
> names(nn1_iristrain)[6] <- "setosa"
> names(nn1_iristrain)[7] <- "versicolor"
> names(nn1_iristrain)[8] <- "virginica"
> head(nn1_iristrain[,5:8])
      Species setosa versicolor virginica
71 versicolor  FALSE       TRUE     FALSE
13     setosa   TRUE      FALSE     FALSE
```

145	virginica	FALSE	FALSE	TRUE
84	versicolor	FALSE	TRUE	FALSE
3	setosa	TRUE	FALSE	FALSE
105	virginica	FALSE	FALSE	TRUE

Next, we'll train the model based on the reconfigured training set using all four feature variables. We also have the opportunity to define the required number of hidden layers and hidden neurons according to the needed complexity. The complexity of the calculated function increases with the addition of hidden layers or hidden neurons. The default value is one hidden layer with one hidden neuron. We'll use the argument `hidden=c(4)` to indicate a single hidden layer with four hidden neurons. You can experiment with different numbers of hidden layers with different number of neurons each. For example, you might try `hidden=c(2,4,2)` which specifies three hidden layers, with two, four, and two neurons respectively. When you run the algorithm, you may notice it takes a while to complete even with a very modestly sized data set. This is because the algorithm is fairly compute intensive. The more hidden layers, the longer it should take. In some cases, the algorithm may not converge, and you may have to go back and change the number of hidden layers and/or neurons per layer.

In the call to `neuralnet()` below, we're using the default value of "rprop+" for the `algorithm` argument. This refers to traditional back propagation. There are a number of other algorithm options that you can experiment with depending on predictive accuracy of the neural network for your problem domain.

```
> nn1 <- neuralnet(setosa+versicolor+virginica ~
    Sepal.Length+Sepal.Width+Petal.Length+Petal.Width,
    data=nn1_iristrain, hidden=c(4))
```

The trained neural network object nn1 is an object of class nn. You'll find that this class of object contains a number of basic information components about the training process and the trained neural network. This includes all information that has to be known to reproduce the results such as the starting weights. You can also just use the `print(nn1)` function to see that the training process needed 20,533 steps before it was able to converge.

```
> print(nn1)
Call: neuralnet(formula = setosa + versicolor + virginica ~
     Sepal.Length +    Sepal.Width + Petal.Length + Petal.Width, data
     = nn1_iristrain,    hidden = c(4))
1 repetition was calculated.
Error Reached Threshold Steps
1 0.9297848198   0.009291227594 20533
```

Other components found in the neural net object `nn1` are listed here:

- `nn1$response` – extracted from the `data` argument are the three binary variables we configured above.
- `nn1$covariate` – variables extracted from the `data` argument, basically the values for `Sepal.Length`, `Sepal.Width`, `Petal.Length` and `Petal.Width`.
- `nn1$data` – a copy of the `data` argument.
- `nn1$net.result` – the output of the neural network, i.e. fitted values.
- `nn1$weights` – list containing the fitted weights of the neural network for reach replication.
- `nn1$generalized.weights` – list containing the fitted weights of the neural network.
- `nn1$result.matrix` – a matrix containing the error reached threshold.
- `nn1$startweights` – a list containing the starting weights.

The `neuralnet` package also has a `plot()` function to visualize the neural network. Figure 6-9 has a plot of the `nn1` object. It reflects the structure of the trained neural network, i.e., network topology. By default, the plot includes the trained synaptic weights, all intercepts, as well as basic information about the training process like the overall error and the number of steps need to reach convergence.

```
> plot(nn1)
```

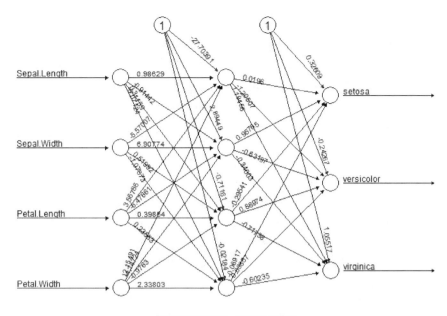

Error: 0.908707   Steps: 14169

Figure 6-9 Plot of a trained neural network showing the hidden layer consisting of four hidden neurons

Next, let's use the trained neural network to predict response variables for the test set. We can use the `compute()` function on the `nn1` object produced by `neuralnet()`. This function computes the outputs of all neurons for specific arbitrary predictor vectors (in this case `test_iris`), given a trained neural network. Remember to make sure that the order of the predictors is the same in the test set data frame as in the original neural network.

```
> prediction <- compute(nn1, test_iris[-5])
> prediction <- prediction$net.result
```

The next step is to set up a character vector containing the response variable values (Species) predicted by the neural network and create a confusion matrix with the `table()` function to check the accuracy of the model by comparing the predicted response with the actual. We can visually inspect the matrix to see there were only a handful of misclassifications.

```
> pred_idx <- function(x) {return(which(x==max(x)))}
> idx <- apply(prediction, c(1), pred_idx)
> prediction_nn <- c('setosa', 'versicolor', 'virginica')[idx]
```

```
> xtab <- table(prediction_nn, test_iris$Species)
> xtab
prediction_nn setosa versicolor virginica
    setosa          20          0          0
    versicolor       0         18          2
    virginica        0          3         17
```

ENSEMBLES

Ensemble methods have become an important addition to the data scientist's toolbox. The technique is so popular that it is often the strategy of choice for participants of machine learning competitions such as Kaggle, where many of the winning solutions are based on variations of the ensemble method strategy. Basically, ensemble methods are statistical learning algorithms that achieve enhanced predictive performance by constructing a set of classifiers, usually small decision trees, and then classifying new data points by taking a weighted vote of their predictions. In other words, instead of picking a single model, ensemble methods combine multiple models in a certain way to fit the training data. There are two primary ways this can occur: *bagging* and *boosting.*

In bagging, we create multiple copies of the original training set using a technique called "the bootstrap," fitting a separate decision tree to each copy, and then combining all of the trees in order to create a single predictive model. After multiple models are trained, we use a voting scheme to predict future data. Boosting works in a similar manner except that the trees are grown sequentially, i.e., each tree is grown using information from previously grown trees. Boosting does not use bootstrap sampling; rather, each tree is fit on a modified version of the original data set.

To conceptualize the ensemble process, think of how groups of people can often make better decisions than individuals especially when group members each come in with their own biases. The same is true in machine learning. A nice characteristic of ensembles is that you can often get away with using much simpler learners and still achieve great performance. In essence, an ensemble is a supervised learning technique for combining many *weak learners* in an attempt to produce a *strong learner*.

A good example of the power of bagging is posing a question to the audience for *Who Wants to Be a Millionaire*. Each individual audience member has some information about what the correct answer is and has a better-than-random chance of guessing the correct answer. Even if each individual audience member has a high probability of guessing incorrectly, it is still unlikely that the plurality of the audience will be wrong. The analogy also points out some limitations of bagging. First, the individual classifiers have to be informative. Asking the audience doesn't work if no one in the audience has knowledge of the subject and people guess completely at random. Second, bagging doesn't give you much, if anything, if some of the composite classifiers are already strong predictors on their own. If you knew that one person in the audience had a high probability of getting the answer correct, you'd rather just ask that one person than polling the whole audience. Bagging is most appropriate in situations where there are many mediocre classifiers but it's difficult to find a single exceptional classifier.

Evaluating the prediction produced by an ensemble is typically more computation intensive than evaluating the prediction of a single model, so in a sense ensembles may be thought of as a way to compensate for poor learning algorithms by performing a lot of extra computation. Well-performing machine learning algorithms such as classification trees are commonly used with ensembles. A good example of how ensemble methods are commonly used to solve tough data science problems is the *random forest* algorithm we'll discuss in the next section.

As mentioned earlier, one popular ensemble method that's frequently used in machine learning is called *bagging* (also known as *bootstrap aggregating*), which involves having each model in the ensemble vote with equal weight. In order to promote model variance, bagging trains each model in the ensemble using a randomly drawn subset of the training set. Bagging also reduces variance and helps to avoid overfitting. As an example, the *random forest* algorithm combines collections of random decision trees (i.e., forests) with bagging to achieve very high classification accuracy. If you have enough trees, the random ones will wash out as noise, and only the good trees will have an effect on the final classification.

Boosting, on the other hand, is a type of ensemble method that involves incrementally building an ensemble by training each new model instance to emphasize the training instances that previous models misclassified. The boosting process begins by fitting a simple classifier on the original data set, giving each observation an equal weight. After fitting the first model, classification errors are computed, and the data is assigned new weights to give previously wrongly classified examples a higher weight than correctly classified examples. Observations are incrementally reweighted at each step to give greater weight to observations that the previous model wrongly classified. Boosting works by incrementally refining the decision boundary of the aggregate classifier; contrast this to bagging, which works by reducing variance. The final prediction will be voted by each tree learned at each iteration weighted by the accuracy of that tree. In some cases, boosting has been shown to yield better predictive accuracy than bagging, but it also tends to be more likely to overfit the training data.

Blending is the simplest and most intuitive way to combine different models. Blending involves taking the predictions of several composite models and including them in a larger model such as a second stage linear or logistic regression. Blending can be used on any type of composite models but is more appropriate when the composite models are fewer and more complex than in boosting or bagging. What properties blending has depends on exactly how models are combined. If a simple linear regression is used, this is equivalent to taking a weighted average of all predictions and works simply by reducing variance. If models are combined using logistic regression, neural network, or even linear regressions with interactions, then composite models are able to have multiplicative effects on one another.

Whether it's appropriate to use an ensemble and what kind depends on the specific problem that you're trying to solve. Throwing lots of models at a problem and combining all of their predictions is rarely ever a good substitute for domain knowledge, but it can be quite useful when domain knowledge or availability of highly salient features is poor. Ensembling also tends to make models less easy to interpret, but still easier to interpret than black box models like neural networks.

A good way to get up to speed with the power of ensemble methods is by experimenting with R's `randomForest()` algorithm for classification and regression that is a part of the Fortran original by Leo Breiman and Adele Cutler. In the next section, we'll discuss how to perform classification with the random forest algorithm.

RANDOM FORESTS

As mentioned in the previous section, the *random forest* algorithm is one of the most popular and commonly used bagging methods. In addition to selecting training data out of the training data set at each decision node of the tree, the algorithm randomly selects a number of feature variables and learns a decision tree from it. Finally, each tree in the forest votes for the most popular class.

Behind the scenes, random forests are a type of recursive partitioning method particularly well-suited to problems with a small number of observations with a large number of feature variables. They involve an ensemble, i.e., a set of classification trees that are calculated on random subsets of the data, using a subset of randomly restricted and selected predictors for each split in each classification tree. In this way, random forests are able to better examine the contribution and behavior that each predictor yields, even when one predictor's effect would usually be overshadowed by more significant competitors in simpler models. Furthermore, the results of an ensemble of classification trees have been shown to produce better predictions than the results of one classification tree on its own.

Random forests are a truly "random" statistical method in that the model results can vary from run to run. Therefore, it is important that you verify the stability of your forests by starting with at least one different seed value and by increasing the size of your forest to a sufficiently large number.

As an example, let's use random forests to classify the `iris` data set. First, we need to install the `randomForest` package and open the library for use.

```
> install.packages("randomForest")
> library(randomForest)
```

Next, we'll call the algorithm using the `randomForest()` function. The arguments we'll use are the `formula` describing the model to be fitted, namely Species~. which says we're classifying Species using the four predictors in the data set. We'll also specify the data frame to use for training the model with data=train_iris. The argument ntree=500 specifies the number of trees to grow. This should not be set to too small a number in order to ensure that every input row gets predicted at least a few times. We use mtry=2 to specify the number of variables randomly sampled as candidates at each split. The default value for classification is the square root of the number of variables. Finally, we use importance=TRUE to tell the algorithm to assess the importance of the predictors.

```
> rf <- randomForest(Species~., data=train_iris, ntree=500, mtry=2,
    importance=TRUE)
```

Now we can use the trained model rf to classify the test set test_iris. We'll use the predict() function for this purpose. We can then generate a confusion matrix with table() in order to compare the predicted versus actual classifications. We need for the misclassification error to be low. In this case, we see there were only three misclassifications.

```
> prediction <- predict(rf, newdata=test_iris, type="class")
> table(prediction, test_iris$Species)
prediction   setosa versicolor virginica
  setosa        20         0          0
  versicolor     0        20          2
  virginica      0         1         17
```

Since we asked the algorithm to assess the importance of the predictors, we can retrieve this information that's stored in the random forest object rf by using either rf$importance or the importance(rf) function. The importance component of rf contains a matrix with a number of columns equal to the number of classes plus two—in this case, five columns. The first three columns are the class-specific measures computed as mean decrease in accuracy. The fourth column is the mean decrease in accuracy over all classes. The last column is the mean decrease in Gini index (a measure of total variance across classes in the model).

```
> importance(rf)
                    setosa    versicolor    virginica
    MeanDecreaseAccuracy

Sepal.Length 0.04522895   0.021642010 0.071957664
    0.046288212

Sepal.Width  0.00523258  -0.003301299 0.006098693
    0.002920681

Petal.Length 0.31637557   0.290288009 0.354026892
    0.316221928

Petal.Width  0.30126501   0.249734399 0.286229751
    0.275835179

                 MeanDecreaseGini
Sepal.Length          6.852732
Sepal.Width           1.407675
Petal.Length         27.888180
Petal.Width          23.093445
```

higher #'s are better?

The print() function for random forest objects offers a summary of the analysis. The summary re-iterates the analysis details and tells us what the OOB (Out-of-Bag) error rate is for all cases and the three classes.

```
print(rf)
Call:
  randomForest(formula = Species ~ ., data = train_iris, ntree =
    500, mtry = 2, importance = TRUE)
              Type of random forest: classification
                    Number of trees: 500
No. of variables tried at each split: 2


        OOB estimate of error rate: 6.67%
Confusion matrix:
           setosa versicolor virginica class.error
setosa         30          0         0  0.00000000
versicolor      0         26         3  0.10344828
virginica       0          3        28  0.09677419
```

The `varImpPlot()` function provides a dot chart of variable importance as measured by a random forest. This plot allows you to understand which variables are important and which are weak. The random forest algorithm allows you to look at how much each variable contributes to decreasing node impurity on average. The more a variable contributes, the more useful it is. The variable importance plot in Figure 6-10 shows that the order of importance (with respect to the classes) is the same for the accuracy and Gini index plots. We see that `Petal.Length` followed by `Petal.Width` are the most important.

```
> varImpPlot(rf)
```

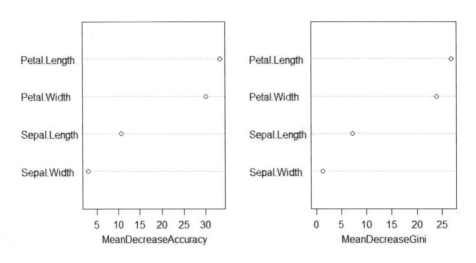

Figure 6-10 Variable importance plot for random forest

Lastly, the importance plots are supported by the `varUsed()` counts, i.e., finding out how many times each predictor variable was actually used in the random forest. This function returns an integer vector containing frequencies that variables are used in the forest. In this example, the rank order is `Petal.Length` (528), `Petal.Width` (414), `Sepal.Length` (1010), and `Sepal.Width` (903).

```
> varUsed(rf, by.tree=FALSE, count=TRUE)
[1] 528 414 1010 903
```

GRADIENT BOOSTING MACHINES

The last classification algorithm we'll consider is called *Gradient Boosting Machines* (GBM), one of the most popular boosting methods. The GBM concept was originally devised by Jerome Friedman, and R's implementation is based on this original work. Boosting is another approach for improving the predictive capabilities of decision trees. Technically, GBM can take on other forms, but decision trees are the dominate usage and R's implementation is internally represented as a tree. The boosted characteristic is derived from the use of multiple weak models combined algorithmically. GBM is considered "gradient boosted" as the algorithm iteratively solves residuals. Bagging involves creating multiple copies of the original training set using the bootstrap method, fitting a separate decision tree to each copy, and then combining all of the trees in order to create a single predictive model. Boosting operates in a similar manner except that the trees are grown sequentially— each tree is grown using information from previously grown trees. Notably, boosting does not involve bootstrap sampling; instead, each tree is fit on a modified version of the original data set.

GBM can be further characterized in the following ways:

- Can be considered competitive with high-performance algorithms like random forests

- Maintains reliable predictive performance, where it is rare to produce worse predictions than simpler models, and avoids nonsensical predictions

- Frequently used by Kaggle competition winners including the Heritage Health Prize

- Explicitly handles missing data, e.g., NAs

- Feature scaling is unnecessary

- Handles more factor levels than random forest (1024 vs. 32)

- No known limit to the number of feature variables

Boosting for classification includes three tuning parameters as shown below that can be passed to the `gbm()` algorithm. You can use roughly the same parameter values to start unless it is suspected that the data set might have peculiar characteristics.

- Shrinkage parameter (`shrinkage`): A small positive number controlling the rate at which boosting learns. From another perspective, shrinkage can be viewed as a regularization parameter dictating how fast/aggressive the algorithm moves across the loss gradient. A value of 0.05 is somewhat aggressive, whereas the default is 0.001. Values less than 0.1 tend to produce good results. Decreasing shrinkage generally improves results but requires more trees, so `shrinkage` and `n.trees` should be adjusted in tandem. In practice, values of 0.01 or 0.001 are common, but the best choice usually depends on the problem being solved.

- Number of trees (`n.trees`): Total number of trees to fit. Care should be taken when selecting this parameter since a value that's too large can result in overfitting (unlike with bagging and random forests). If overfitting occurs at all, it will tend to happen slowly. You can scale back later for predictions if desired or if overfitting is suspected.

- Number of splits in each tree (`interaction.depth`): This parameter controls the complexity of the boosted ensemble. More generally, this parameter controls the interaction order of the boosted model. In practice, a value of 1 often works well.

One main difference between boosting and random forests is with boosting smaller trees are typically sufficient since growth of a particular tree takes into account the other trees that have already been grown. Using smaller trees also can help with interpretability.

In order to demonstrate boosting, we'll use the `gbm` package and its `gbm()` algorithm. We'll start by installing and loading the library.

```
> install.packages("gbm")
> library(gbm)
```

Now we can invoke the `gbm()` algorithm to predict the variable `Species` using the rest of the `iris` data set variables as predictors. We'll specify the number of trees with the `n.trees=2000` argument. Although `gbm()` offers many distribution choices (loss functions), we'll use "multinomial" for classification when there are more than two classes. The `shrinkage` argument value is set to 0.01 per the recommendations above. Next, we can print the results of the model.

```
> gbm1 <- gbm(Species ~ ., distribution="multinomial",
data=train_iris, n.trees=2000, shrinkage=0.01)
> gbm1
gbm(formula = Species ~ ., distribution = "multinomial", data =
    train_iris,
  n.trees = 2000, shrinkage = 0.01)
A gradient boosted model with multinomial loss function.
2000 iterations were performed.
There were four predictors, of which four had non-zero influence.
```

Using the `gbm1` object, we can make predictions for the `test_iris` data set using `predict.gbm()`. Notice that this function returns a matrix of class probabilities, one column for each species.

```
> prediction <- predict.gbm(gbm1, test_iris, type="response",
    n.trees=1000)
```

Finally, we can use the `summary.gbm()` function for the GBM algorithm, which also produces a plot as shown in Figure 6-11 that indicates the relative influence for each predictor. Here, `Petal.Length` and `Petal.Width` have the most influence.

```
> summary.gbm(gbm1)
                     var    rel.inf
Petal.Length Petal.Length 69.845854
Petal.Width   Petal.Width 21.582802
Sepal.Length Sepal.Length  4.440778
Sepal.Width   Sepal.Width  4.130565
```

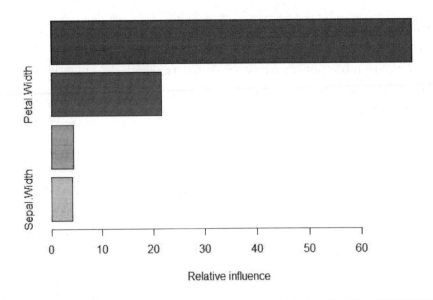

Figure 6-11 GBM summary() results showing relative influence

SUMMARY

In this chapter we continued our examination of supervised machine learning with a number of frequently used methods of classification—the problem of identifying to which of a set of categories (sub-populations) a new observation belongs. Classification is probably the most recognizable statistical learning technique because it is used for a wide range of problem domains such as spam detection, churn prediction, fraud detection, and so many others. We considered a number of popular forms of classification in this chapter: logistic regression, classification trees, naïve Bayes, K-nearest neighbors, support vector machines, neural networks, ensemble methods, random forests, and gradient boosting machines. Next, in Chapter 7, we'll explore techniques for evaluating the performance of statistical learning algorithms including regression and classification.

Here is a summary of what you've learned in this chapter:

- We began with a simple classification example using the spam data set in the `kernlab` package. We introduced classification concepts without using an established algorithm.

- Using the algorithm for generalized linear models - `glm()`, we explored logistic regression, which models the probability that the response belongs to a particular category or class.
- We used the `tree()` algorithm from the `tree` package to experiment with classification trees. We then used the trained classifier to make predictions with the test set.
- We saw the Bayes classifier, a learning method that is based on conditional probability. We trained a model using the `naiveBayes()` function in the `e1071` package and used it to make predictions.
- We learned how to apply the K-nearest neighbors algorithm, an example of instance based learning, using the `knn()` function from the `class` package.
- We were provided with a non-mathematical motivation for the support vector machines method of statistical learning and saw an example using the `svm()` algorithm from the `e1071` package.
- We explored the use of neural networks to solve non-linear classification problems and used the `neuralnet()` function found in the `neuralnet` package as an example.
- We finished the chapter by looking at two popular ensemble methods, Random Forests and Gradient Boosting Machines.

Chapter 7
Evaluating Model Performance

In this chapter we shall explore the process of evaluating the results delivered by a machine learning algorithm and offer various techniques for obtaining better model performance. When we speak of assessing how well a model performs, we generally think of fit measure (R^2, adjusted R^2, RMSE, etc.), but what we really would like to know is how well a particular model predicts based on new data. This notion finds its basis in the scientific method where observation yields description and experimentation yields explanation—using statistical learning models with the goal of explanation and/or prediction. When predictions are confirmed, evidence is born for supporting a theory. When predictions fail, evidence is born for rejecting a theory.

The methods discussed in this chapter will serve to complete the "data science" process as defined in Chapter 1 (see Figure 1-2). But before you dive into project presentations or "data storytelling," you may need to iterate the data science process by evaluating model performance, taking what you've learned, and revisiting previous steps: data munging, feature selection, EDA and statistical analysis, and even model selection (since your evaluation results may tell you that you chose the wrong algorithm to begin with).

In reality, the data science process never stops. You should continually reevaluate your models with new data as they become available, and consequently retrain your algorithms with enhanced tuning parameters in order to obtain better predictive power.

In terms of model selection, we can view this part of the data science process in a different light now that we've seen the rest of the process. We often have many candidate models (regression, decision tree, neural net, SVM, random forest, etc.). Each model may have to be *tuned* for optimal prediction performance. In order to choose the (approximate) best model, we need to estimate objectively the performance of different models. The performance metric is usually the *test error rate*, also called the *generalization error*, which is the expected prediction error over an independent test sample. In contrast, the *training error rate* is the expected prediction error over the training sample, which is not an objective performance measure since a model can be overfit to the training sample but have poor performance on new data.

Once we decide on a best model, we want to estimate its test error rate by making predictions on a new sample that provides an objective judgement on the performance of the chosen model. The estimated test error rate is typically larger, albeit closer to the truth, than the one obtained at the original model selection stage of the data science process. This is because the very action of choosing the best model according to the estimated test errors across all candidate models is equivalent to training at the risk of overfitting (a topic covered in the next section) on the validation portion of the data that generates the test errors.

In the sections of this chapter that follow, we'll explore a variety of model performance methods that you can add to your data science toolbox. Hopefully, as you gain more experience with machine learning, you'll acquire even more methods designed to handle new circumstances. Ultimately, you'll have a variety of techniques to apply to ensure that your algorithms are operating at peak predictive capabilities.

OVERFITTING

Probably the most common problem surrounding the performance of machine learning algorithms is *overfitting*. Certain applications of statistical learning tend to cause specific models to perform very poorly due to overfitting, and it is at this stage of the data science process to evaluate whether overfitting is in play. In a sense, a model is overfit when it matches part of the noise in a data set rather than the true underlying signal. More concretely, overfitting is the situation where an algorithm is trained too well for accuracy with a specific training data set. If tailored too specifically to a training data set, the algorithm fails to generalize well and its predictive power is reduced for any new data. In other words, when a given algorithm yields a small training set error but a large test set error, we are said to be overfitting the data.

We can discuss overfitting in terms of two key concepts: the *in sample error* (the error rate you get on the training set, i.e., the data set you used to train your model) and the *out of sample error* (the error rate you get on a new data set, which is known as the test set). In the machine learning literature, this is sometimes called the *resubstitution error*. The in sample error is typically going to be optimistic versus the error you would get on a new sample. The reason for this is because your algorithm will "tune" itself for the noise found in the training data set. So when you get a new data set, there will be different noise and the accuracy will be diminished to some small extent. In comparison, the out of sample error is the error rate you get on a new data set—the test set. This is sometimes called the *generalization error*. The idea is that once you build a model on a known training set, you will want to test it on a new data set that is collected by different means—a different time, a different set of observations—to see how well the machine learning algorithm will perform on the new data, i.e., how well the algorithm will generalize.

There are several fundamental aspects to the training set/test set circumstances you need to be concerned about. First, the out of sample error is what you care about most. If you only know the error rate upon which the machine learning algorithm was built, then you know it is very optimistic and probably won't reflect how the model will perform in practice. Next, the in sample error is always going to be less than the out of sample error. Finally, these characteristics are due to "overfitting," i.e., you might be matching the algorithm too well to the training data, since it contains some noise, rather than underlying trends. Thus, when you apply the data to the real world, you're not matching the generalized reality. Sometimes, you may wish to give up some accuracy on your training set just so that you'll have more generalized accuracy on new data.

On the flip side of this issue of predictive accuracy, when a model isn't complex enough to even fit the training set very well, we call this problem *underfitting* and the algorithm is said to have *high bias*. (We'll examine bias and variance in more depth in the next section.) Both terms mean we're not fitting the training data very well.

As a quick example of bias, consider the situation where you're fitting a straight line through some data points in order to predict housing prices based on size (in square feet) of the home. There is a very strong preconception, or strong bias, that the housing prices are going to vary linearly with size. Despite the data that may be to the contrary of this preconception, the bias causes the algorithm to fit a straight line, which ends up being a poor fit to the data. As we saw in Chapter 5, we can use polynomial regression to fit a curve through all of the training examples. This seems to do a very good job (really, it tries too hard) fitting the training set, but it might not be a good model for housing prices. Once again, this problem is called overfitting, and the algorithm is said to have *high variance*. The intuition for variance is that if we're fitting such a high order polynomial, then the hypothesis can fit almost any function, and the space of possible hypotheses is too large, too variable. And we don't have enough data to constrain it to give us a good hypothesis. Somewhere in the middle of these two extremes is considered "just right."

Overfitting also can be caused if we have too many feature variables where the learned hypothesis may fit the training set very well but fails to generalize to new examples (i.e., predict prices on new examples).

Overfitting can affect classification problems too, say by using the logistic regression algorithm. In this case, underfitting arises when your decision boundary doesn't separate the classes well. At the other extreme, with overfitting you might find a decision boundary that contorts itself to fit every training example.

To illustrate overfitting using R, we'll utilize the `spam` data set found in the `kernlab` package. As we saw in Chapter 5, this data set is used to build and test a spam classifier algorithm. The `spam` data set contains a number of variables that characterize e-mail messages which may contain spam. Recall the data set contains 57 feature variables plus one class label having a value of either "spam" or "nonspam." One useful feature variable is `capitalAve` that might characterize a spam e-mail if this variable's value is high. We'll define two hand-made algorithms using simple rules; one will be overfit to the training set and the other will not be overfit. To start, we'll load the `kernlab` package (install it if you haven't already done so). Then we'll select an arbitrary seed value for reproducible results. Using the `sample()` function, we'll take a small sample of 10 observations and assign the subset to the data frame `sampleSpam`.

```
> install.packages("kernlab")
> library(kernlab)
```

```
> data(spam) # 4601 observations x 58 variables
> set.seed(333)
> sampleIndex <- sample(dim(spam)[1], size=10)
> sampleSpam <- spam[sampleIndex,]
```

Next, it is a good idea to perform some quick EDA to become familiar with the sample data set. We can produce a useful plot of sampleSpam$capitalAve to understand the distribution of the data. To do this, we need a way of indicating whether each data point is spam or nonspam; we can use the pch argument of the plot() function for this purpose. We'll encode labels with "nonspam" with a value 1 and "spam" with a value 2. These values conveniently translate to pch symbols for a circle and triangle, respectively.

```
> spamSymbol <- (sampleSpam$type=="spam") + 1
> plot(sampleSpam$capitalAve, pch=spamSymbol)
> legend('topright', legend=c("nonspam", "spam"), pch=c(1,2))
```

The plot shown in Figure 7-1 below has a fairly nice distribution of spam and nonspam data points, with the exception of the last one that is circled. Here are the values for each capitalAve in the sample:

```
> sampleSpam$capitalAve
[1] 1.000 11.320 1.000 1.840 7.300 1.635 2.666 3.545 5.163 2.444
```

Now let's consider a hand-made algorithm with some simple rules to classify the data points. The first two rules are very general and will manage to identify all of the spam e-mails except the problem one that's circled with a value of 2.444. The problem with overfitting is fine tuning the algorithm so that it predicts the training set perfectly. So we add a couple more rules that take into account the problem data point.

```
> alg1 <- function(x){
pred <- rep(NA, length(x))
pred[x>2.7] <- "spam"
pred[x<2.4] <- "nonspam"
# Additional rules result in overfitting
pred[x<=2.45 & x>=2.4] <- "spam"
```

```
pred[x<=2.7 & x>2.45] <- "nonspam"
return(pred)

}
```

The confusion matrix we get for predicted versus actual labels shows a perfect 5 spams and 5 nonspams. No data points have been misclassified.

```
> table(alg1(sampleSpam$capitalAve),sampleSpam$type)

         nonspam spam
nonspam       5    0
spam          0    5
```

Now we define a second algorithm that does not overfit with the training set. This time, the confusion matrix shows the one expected misclassification.

```
> alg2 <- function(x){
  pred <- rep(NA, length(x))
  pred[x>2.8] <- "spam"
  pred[x<=2.8] <- "nonspam"
  return(pred)

}
> table(alg2(sampleSpam$capitalAve),sampleSpam$type)

         nonspam spam
nonspam       5    1
spam          0    4
```

Next, we can see how well the two algorithms generalize to the full spam dataset. Not surprisingly alg1() makes many mistakes since it was trained so specifically to the small training set. We can easily compute the number of errors (1235). Now, running alg2() on the full spam data set, we see it misclassified 1206 observations. This should not be a surprise. The overfit algorithm made more mistakes on the full dataset versus the algorithm that was more generalized.

```
> table(alg1(spam$capitalAve), spam$type)

         nonspam spam
nonspam     2141  588
```

```
spam          647 1225
> sum(alg1(spam$capitalAve)!=spam$type)   # Number of errors
[1] 1235
> table(alg2(spam$capitalAve), spam$type)

         nonspam spam
nonspam    2224  642
spam        564 1171
> sum(alg2(spam$capitalAve)!=spam$type)   # Number of errors
[1] 1206
```

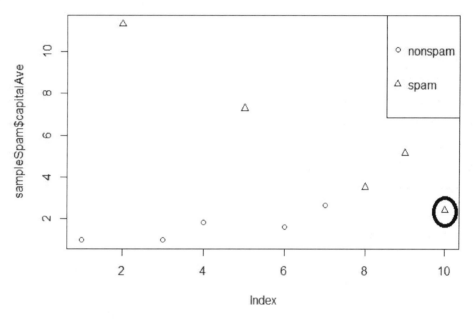

Figure 7 1 EDA plot for capitalAve variable in the training set. If we address the circled data point, overfitting occurs.

If we think that overfitting is occurring, what can we do to address it? For some statistical learning problems, we have a lot of features, and with so many features it becomes hard to visualize (i.e., plot) the data. If we have a lot of features and very little training data, then overfitting can become a problem.

To address the problem of overfitting, there are two main options. The first is to try to reduce the number of features. Here, we can manually select which features to keep, or you can engage a model selection algorithm to automatically decide which features to keep and which features to eliminate.

This idea of decreasing the number of features can work well and reduce overfitting. The disadvantage is that by throwing away some of the features, you're also throwing away some of the information about the problem—maybe some of the features are useful for making predictions.

The second option is a process called *regularization*. Here, we keep all the features but reduce the magnitude of the feature variable values. This method works well when we have a lot of features, each of which contributes a small degree in making the prediction. With regularization, the estimated coefficients are shrunk towards zero relative to the least squares estimates. This effect is often called *shrinkage* and has the effect of reducing variance. Some regularization methods may result in the estimating of some coefficients to be exactly zero, which, as a result, indirectly performs feature selection. Regularization ultimately prevents overfitting by restraining our model from matching noise in the training data we use to fit it.

In R, two commonly used regularization methods for shrinking the regression coefficients toward zero are *ridge regression* and the *lasso*. Using the `glmnet()` algorithm that fits linear models using regularization, you can use the `alpha` argument to select the desired method: if `alpha=0` then a ridge regression model is fit, whereas if `alpha=1` then a lasso model is fit. `glmnet()` also has a tuning parameter called `lambda` which controls the impact of regularization. You can experiment with different values of the regularization parameter `lambda` on a training set and see how it performs on the test set by reviewing the out of sample error. We'll see how to compute error rates later in this chapter. Note that large, intermediate and small values of `lambda` can affect the high bias (underfit) and high variance (overfit) problems discussed in the next section. Generally, well-chosen intermediate values of `lambda` will produce a good balance of bias and variance. You can start by iterating `lambda` from 0 to 10 in steps of 0.02 and see how well the algorithm performs for each value. Model selection occurs by using the regularization parameter that minimizes the out of sample error (test set error).

BIAS AND VARIANCE

In machine learning, we hold the assumption that the underlying data of a problem follows some mathematical model, and during the training process we try to fit the training data into this assumed model and determine the optimal model parameters that keep the error to a minimum. But if you run a learning algorithm and it doesn't do as well as you were hoping (due to high cross-validation or test errors), almost all the time it is because you either have a high bias problem or a high variance problem—in other words, an underfitting problem or an overfitting problem. It is important to determine whether it is high bias, high variance, or a bit of both. Knowing what is happening will give you a strong indicator for which methods should be employed to improve your algorithm's performance.

One source of error occurs when our assumed model is fundamentally wrong, e.g., we try to model a non-linear relationship with a linear model. Simple models tend to under-fit since they're not flexible enough to model the true relationship. This is known as a *high bias problem*, where we use an over simplified model to represent the underlying data. Another source of error is when the model parameters fits too specifically to the training data and do not generalize well to the underlying data pattern (i.e., yields a high generalization error). This is generally true of more complex models that exhibit the *high variance problem*, which leads to overfitting. The key is to achieve a balance between bias and variance when you're evaluating the performance of your algorithm.

The *bias-variance tradeoff* problem is an important aspect of data science projects based on machine learning. In order to simplify the discussion of this topic but still provide useful insights, let's consider an explanation of the bias-variance tradeoff that avoids mathematical equations (although equations can be quite satisfying!).

To approximate reality, a learning algorithm uses mathematical models whose "error" can be split into two main components: a *reducible error* and an *irreducible error*. Irreducible error is noise that cannot be eliminated by modeling and is associated with a natural variability in a system. On the other hand, reducible error, as the name suggests, can be and should be minimized further to maximize the model's accuracy.

Reducible error can be further decomposed into "error due to squared bias" and "error due to variance." The data scientist's goal is to simultaneously achieve low variance and low bias as much as possible in order to obtain as accurate model as is feasible. Note that variance is inherently a nonnegative quantity, and squared bias is also nonnegative. However, there is a tradeoff to be made when selecting models of different flexibility or complexity and in selecting appropriate training sets to minimize these sources of error.

The *error due to squared bias* is the amount by which the expected model prediction differs from the true value or target over the training data. Essentially, bias refers to the error that is introduced by approximating a real-life problem (which could be complicated) with a much simpler model. Because of this particular definition, we tend to think of bias as being introduced at the model selection step in the data science process. Data scientists can repeat the model building process (through resampling) to obtain the average of prediction values. If these average prediction values are substantially different than the true value, bias will be high.

The *error due to variance* is the amount by which the prediction over one training set differs from the expected predicted value over all the training sets. Ideally, the predicted value should not vary too much between training sets. However, if a model has high variance, then small changes in the training data can result in large changes in predicted value. As with bias, you can repeat the entire model building process multiple times. Essentially, variance measures how inconsistent the predictions are from one another over different training sets, not whether they are accurate. Another important point is with highly correlated feature variables that can lead to *collinearity* issues, which in turn lead to greatly increased variance.

Models that exhibit small variance and high bias are seen to *underfit* the truth target. Models that exhibit high variance and low bias, on the other hand, *overfit* the truth target. As indicated earlier, if your target truth is highly nonlinear and you select a linear model to approximate it, then you're introducing a bias resulting from the linear model's inability to capture nonlinearity. In other words, your linear model is *underfitting* the nonlinear target function over the training set. Likewise, if your target truth is linear and you select a nonlinear model to approximate it, then you're introducing a bias resulting from the nonlinear model's inability to be linear where it needs to be. In fact, the nonlinear model is *overfitting* the linear target function over the training set.

The "tradeoff" between bias and variance can be viewed in this manner: a learning algorithm with low bias must be "flexible" so that it can fit the data well. But if the learning algorithm is too flexible, it will fit each training data set differently and hence have high variance. As a general rule, as we use more flexible models, the variance will increase and the bias will decrease. A key characteristic of many supervised learning methods is a built-in way to control the bias-variance tradeoff either automatically or by providing a special parameter that the data scientist can adjust.

When working to characterize the *bias-variance tradeoff*, you need to develop metrics for determining the accuracy of your model. There are two common metrics used in machine learning: training error rate and test error rate. As an example, for linear regression models you can calculate the Mean Square Error (MSE) for the different data sets – training set to train the model (as mentioned in Chapter 5, typically 60% or even 70% of the available data), and test set to check the accuracy of the model (typically 40% or 30% of the available data). For completeness, there is an additional cross validation step after training. So a typical split is 60% training, 20% cross validation, and 20% test. The training set is for model fitting. The cross validation set is for estimating the prediction error so you can choose the appropriate model. And the test set is used to assess the model (and its error) once the model is chosen.

In Figure 7-2 below, we see a plot of a model's performance using prediction capability on the vertical axis as a function of model complexity on the horizontal axis. Here, we depict the case where we use a number of different orders of polynomial functions (from order 1 to 12) to approximate the target function. Shown in the figure are the calculated squared bias, variance, and test set error for each of the estimator functions.

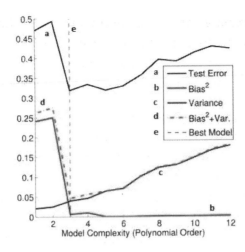

Figure 7-2 Model complexity plot showing test error, squared bias, and variance (from The Clever Machine blog)

The figure shows that as the model's complexity increases, the variance slowly increases and the squared bias decreases. This points to the tradeoff between bias and variance due to model complexity, i.e., models that are too complex tend to have high variance and low bias, while models that are too simple will tend to have high bias and low variance. The goal is to find a model that has both low bias and low variance. In the figure, we see the best model as a dashed vertical line representing the prediction error on the test set. We see that the best estimator function is an order 3 polynomial. Notice that the dashed vertical line is located where the function defined by the sum of the squared bias and variance is also at a minimum.

Managing the bias-variance tradeoff is a prime example of how experienced data scientists are needed to serve an integral role in maximizing the value of enterprise data assets through the process of detailed model evaluation. As evidenced here, knowledge, intuition and finesse is required to solve business problems through use of statistical learning.

CONFOUNDERS

The Merriam-Webster dictionary defines "confound" as "to fail to discern differences between: mix up." Translating this generic definition to the field of data science, we see that a confounder is a variable that is correlated with both the response variable and the predictor variables. As a result of this correlation, confounders can have a large effect in the accuracy of a machine learning problem. In a common regression problem, for instance, confounders can change the regression line or even change the sign of the line.

Two variables are confounded when their effects cannot be separated from each other. When approaching a data science project, this problem is encountered when there is a variable other than the predictor variable that may have caused the effect being studied. The variable causing the confounding reduces the internal validity of the analysis in that one cannot say for sure that the predictor variable caused the effect. This variable changes with the predictor but was not intended to do so. As a result, the effect cannot be attributed to the predictor variable but may well have been caused by the other variable, the confounder.

In some situations, confounded variables are difficult to avoid. Consider, for example, an experimenter effect. Most participants who voluntarily participate in user studies wish the researchers well and hope they succeed. If they know which condition the experimenters favor, they may evaluate it more positively. To avoid having confounded variables, it is important to take possible bias into account, to make sure participants are assigned randomly to experimental conditions, and to verify that the predictor variable is the sole element that can be causing the effect.

Let's consider an example of estimating the causal effect of advertising on sales. The difficulty is that there are many confounding variables, such as seasonality or weather conditions, that cause both increased ad exposures and increased purchases by consumers. Consider the case of an advertising manager who was asked why she thought her ads were effective. In response she came up with a chart that showed that every December she increased her ad spend and sure enough, purchases go up. Of course, in this case seasonality can be included in the model. However, generally there will be other confounding variables that affect both exposure to ads and the propensity of purchase, which makes causal interpretations of observed relationships problematic.

Several approaches can be taken to avoid losing accuracy due to confounded variables. The best approach is to design the project such that confounding variables are avoided. Confounders can sometimes be detected by careful exploration of the data set, e.g., using methods of exploratory data analysis (EDA). Other precautions can be taken that would allow the data scientist to draw valid conclusions. First, one can use demographic data to measure possible confounding. When conducting a consumer study, it is useful to collect additional demographic data so that expected confounding can be objectively evaluated. Systematic differences in such variables between conditions would indicate confounding variables. However, if experimental groups do not differ on these measures, the analysis is strengthened. For example, when evaluating a weight loss system, researchers could collect information about education levels and attitudes toward healthy living. They could then compare whether there are systematic differences between the experimental groups with regard to these variables.

Another approach to avoid making predictions based on confounded variables is to include complementary outcome measures in the study. When such complementary measures are used, contradictions in their outcomes may be an indication that there are confounded variables. Other designs and analyses can take potential confounding into account and even use it. Multivariate statistical analysis can be used to take the effect of confounded variables into account.

It is never too late to consider how confounding variables might be affecting the results delivered by your statistical learning models. If you feel that your algorithm's results aren't what they should be, it is worth your time to take a step back and look for confounders.

DATA LEAKAGE

As a data scientist, you should always be aware of circumstances that may cause your machine learning algorithms to over-represent their generalization error as this may render them useless in the solution of real-world problems. One such potential problem is called *data leakage*, when the data you are using to train a machine learning algorithm happens to have the information you are trying to predict. It is undesirable on many levels as a source of poor generalization and over-estimation of expected performance. Data leakage often occurs subtly and inadvertently, and it may result in overfitting. Many data scientists view data leakage as one of the top machine learning mistakes.

Data leakage can manifest in many ways including:

- Leaking data from the test set into the training set
- Leaking the correct prediction or ground truth into the test data
- Leaking of information from the future into the past
- Reversing obfuscation, randomization, or anonymization of data that was intentionally included
- Information from data samples outside of scope of the algorithm's intended use
- Any of the above existing in external data coupled with the training set

In general, data leakage comes from two sources in a machine learning algorithm: the feature variables and the training set. A trivial example of data leakage would be a model that uses the response variable itself as a predictor, thus concluding, for example, that "it is sunny on sunny days."

As a more concrete example, consider the use of a "customer service rep name" feature variable in a Software as a Service (SaaS) company churn prediction algorithm. Using the name of the rep who interviewed a customer when they churned might seem innocent enough until you find out that a specific rep was assigned to take over customer accounts where customers had already indicated they intended to churn. In this case, the resulting algorithm would be highly predictive of whether the customer had churned but would be useless for making predictions on new customers. This is an extreme example; many more instances of data leakage occur in subtle and hard-to-detect ways. There are war stories of algorithms with data leakage running in production systems for years before the bugs in the data creation or training scripts were detected.

Identifying data leakage beforehand and correcting for it is an important part of improving the definition of a machine learning problem. Many forms of leakage are subtle and are best detected by trying to extract features and train state-of-the-art algorithms on the problem. Here are several strategies to find and eliminate data leakage:

- Exploratory data analysis (EDA) can be a powerful tool for identifying data leakage. EDA allows you to become more intimate with the raw data by examining it through statistical and visualization tools. This kind of examination can reveal data leakage as patterns in the data that are surprising.

- If the performance of your algorithm is too good to be true, data leakage may be the reason. You need to weigh prior or competing documented results with a certain level of performance for the problem at hand. A substantial divergence from this expected performance merits testing the algorithm more closely to establish legitimacy.

- Perform early in-the-field testing of algorithms. Any significant data leakage would be reflected as a difference between estimated and realized out of sample performance. This is perhaps the best approach in identifying data leakage, but it is also the most expensive to implement. It can also be challenging to isolate the cause of such performance discrepancy as data leakage since the cause actually could be classical over-fitting, sampling bias, etc.

Once data leakage has been identified, the next step is to figure out how to fix it (or even if you want to try). For some problems, living with data leakage without attempting to fix it could be acceptable. But if you decide to fix the leakage, care must be taken not to make matters worse. Usually, when there is one leaking feature variable, there are others. Removing the obvious leaks that are detected may exacerbate the effect of undetected ones, and engaging in feature modification in an attempt to plug obvious leaks could create others. The idea is to try to figure out the legitimacy of specific observations and/or feature variables and work to plug the leak and hopefully seal it completely. Rectifying data leakage is an active field of research that will likely yield effective results in the near future.

MEASURING REGRESSION PERFORMANCE

When evaluating the performance of a regression model, we need a metric with which to gauge the accuracy of the prediction. The most commonly used metric for determining the quality of fit is the *root mean square error* (RMSE). RMSE measures the distance between the estimated response variable from the actual response variable. RMSE is defined to be the square root of the mean square error (MSE). MSE in turn is defined as being the sum of the squared differences between the estimated response minus the actual response for each observation in the data set, all divided by the number of observations. MSE penalizes the bigger differences more because of the effect of squaring.

RMSE is a very popular measure of performance for machine learning algorithms, including algorithms that are far more complex than linear regression. In fact, high-profile data science competitions like those hosted by Kaggle and even the seminal Netflix Prize are scored using RMSE as the definitive metric of how well the competitor's algorithm performed.

As mentioned in Chapter 5, common practice is to divide the data set into two pieces. We create a training set consisting of 70% of the observations and the other 30% as the test set. Note that you can't just split the data set in terms of the first 70% of the observations going to the training set and the last 30% going to the test set if there is any sort or ordering to the data. It would be better to populate the training and test set by randomly ordering or shuffling the data set first. However, if your data is already in random order, then you can simply split the data set with the first 70% going to the training set and the last 30% going to the test set.

The next step is to train the algorithm on the training set to yield the linear model parameters mentioned in Chapter 5. With these parameters you can then compute the training error rate using MSE and RMSE that shows how well the algorithm was able to estimate the response variable. Finally, we use the trained algorithm on the test set to yield the test set error.

In order to demonstrate this process of model performance evaluation, let's use the `Prestige` data set once again. Recall this data set is available in the `car` package. As we did in Chapter 5, we'll remove incomplete examples and then split the data set into training and test.

```
> library("car")
> data(Prestige) # 102x6
> Prestige_noNA <- na.omit(Prestige)
> n <- nrow(Prestige_noNA) # Number of observations = 102
> ntrain <- round(n*0.7)  # 70% for training set
> set.seed(333)        # Set seed for reproducible results
```

```
> tindex <- sample(n, ntrain) # Create an index
> prestige_train <- Prestige_noNA[tindex,] # Create training set
> prestige_test <- Prestige_noNA[-tindex,] # Create test set
```

For convenience, we can define a reusable function to calculate the RMSE. The function `rmse` below accepts two arguments `y_hat` and `y`, the predicted and actual response variables respectively.

```
# Calculate RMSE
rmse <- function(y_hat, y)
{
 return(sqrt(mean((y_hat-y)^2)))
}
```

Next, we'll fit a linear model using the training set. Once the model has been fitted, we can use it to calculate the RMSE for the training set. For the `y_hat` argument value passed to `rmse()`, we'll use the `predict()` function's output using the fitted model `lm1` (can also use `lm1$fitted`) and for the `y` argument, we'll use the actual response variable values for the training set, namely `prestige_train$prestige`. We see a RSME value of `6.46309`. Next, we'll do a similar process to compute the RMSE for the test set. Here, for `y_hat` we'll use `predict(lm1, newdata=prestige_test)` and for `y` we'll use the actual values in `prestige_test$prestige`. We see a RSME value of `7.705871`, which is slightly larger than the RMSE for the training set. This is to be expected.

```
> lm1 <- lm(prestige~., data=prestige_train)
> rmse_train <- rmse(predict(lm1),prestige_train$prestige)
> rmse_train
[1] 6.46309
> rmse_test <- rmse(predict(lm1, newdata=prestige_test),
prestige_test$prestige)
> rmse_test
[1] 7.705871
```

The RMSE is more sensitive to the occasional large error than other available measures because the squaring process gives disproportionate weight to very large errors. Further, the RMSE can only be compared between models whose errors are measured in the *same units* (e.g., dollars, kilometers, or cases of wine, etc.). If one model's errors are adjusted for inflation while those of another or not, or if one model's errors are in absolute units while another's are in relative units, their error measures cannot be directly compared. In such cases, you have to convert the errors of both models into comparable units before computing the various measures. This means converting the predictions of one model to the same units as those of the other.

There is no absolute criterion for a "good" value of RMSE; it depends on the units in which the variable is measured and on the degree of predictive accuracy, as measured in those units, which is sought in a particular application. Depending on the choice of units, the RMSE of your best model could be measured as a very large or very small number (and everywhere in between). It makes no sense to declare "the model is good (or bad) because the RMSE is less (or greater) than x" unless you are referring to a specific degree of accuracy that is relevant to your prediction application.

Do not make a fine distinction comparing a model with an RMSE of 6.25, which is not significantly better than one with an RMSE of 6.39. It may be useful to think of this in percentage terms: If one model's RMSE is 35% lower than that of another model, then that is probably very significant. If it is 12% lower, that can be viewed as somewhat significant. But if it is only 3% better, that is probably not significant. These distinctions are especially important when you are trading off model complexity against the error measures: it is probably not worth adding another feature variable to a regression model to decrease the RMSE by only a few more percentage points. The RMSE is a valid indicator of relative model quality, but only if it can be trusted. Note that if there is evidence that the model is *overfitted*, then the RMSE *and all other error measures* may need to be discounted.

One criticism about RMSE is that it's not immediately clear how mediocre performance can be characterized. An RMSE value of 0 yields a perfect performance measure, but the pursuit of perfection is not realistic goal for machine learning. Similarly, it often isn't easy to recognize when a model is performing poorly. For instance, if most house prices are around $250,000 and you predict $5 million, then you'll get a large RMSE value. The unbounded values for RMSE can make it difficult to know whether your model's performance is reasonable. One solution to this problem is to use the R^2 metric that we covered in Chapter 5. The idea of R^2 is to see how much better your model does than just using the mean. To make it easy to interpret, R^2 will always be between 0 and 1. If the model is doing no better than the mean, R^2 will be 0 and if you predict every data point perfectly, then it will be 1.

Because R^2 is always between 0 and 1, data scientists typically multiply the value by 100 and explain it as the percent of the variance in the data you've explained with your model. This is a convenient way to establish an intuition for how accurate your model is even in a problem domain where you have little experience with the standard values of RMSE.

In order to calculate R^2, you need to compute the residual standard error (RSE) for a model that uses only the mean output to make predictions for all of your data. After that, it's a simple process as defined in the following function:

```
> rsquared <- function(y_hat, y){
  mu <- mean(y)
  rse <- mean((y_hat - y)^2) / mean((mu - y)^2)
  rsquared <- (1 - rse)*100
  return(rsquared)
}
```

In the R code below, we can use `rsquared()` to come up with the R^2 values for both the training and test set.

```
> y_hat <- lm1$fitted.values # Calculate R2 for training
> y <- prestige_train$prestige
> rsquared(y_hat, y)
[1] 85.09975
> y_hat <- predict(lm1, newdata=prestige_test) #Calc R2 for test
> y <- prestige_test$prestige
> rsquared(y_hat, y)
[1] 80.71466
```

MEASURING CLASSIFICATION PERFORMANCE

When evaluating the performance of a classification model, we need a metric with which to gauge the accuracy of the prediction. Recall that in classification, there is a target categorical variable such as spam or not spam. There are many commonly used metrics for determining the accuracy of a classifier, but typically we'll use *misclassification rate*. We follow the same procedure as with regression, splitting the data set into a training set of 70% of the observations and a test set of 30%. Then we compute the test set error or misclassification error, i.e., you either make a correct prediction or an incorrect prediction (mislabeled an observation). The misclassification error is just the fraction of the observations in the test set that the model has mislabeled. This is the definition of the test set error using the misclassification error metric.

Considering a binary classification problem where there are two classes (like spam or not spam, fraud or not fraud, churn or not churn, clicked on ad or did not click on ad, etc.), we can break the problem down into the following measures:

- True positive (TP): The model predicts True and the actual outcome is True.
- True negative (TN): The model predicts False and the actual outcome is False.
- False positive (FP): The model predicts True but the actual outcome is False.
- False negative (FN): The model predicts False but the actual outcome is True.

With these measures, we can calculate a variety of metrics that can serve to clarify how well the model is predicting. The classification error rate (misclassification rate) defined below represents the rate at which the model misclassified the observations when considering a binary classification problem. This would be the metric of all misclassifications, i.e., False Negatives plus False Positives, divided by the number of all observations. The goal is to use a model where this metric is minimized.

- *Classification error rate* = (FN + FP) / (TP + TN + FP + FN) is also (1 − accuracy).

- *Accuracy* = (TP + TN) / (TP + TN + FP + FN) is the number of correct classifications out of all predictions.

- *Sensitivity* (also known as *recall* or *true positive rate*) = TP / (TP + FN) measures the proportion of positives that are correctly identified.

- *Specificity* (also known as *true negative rate*) = TN / (FP + TN) measures the proportion of negatives that are correctly identified.

- *Precision* (also known as *positive predictive value*) = TP / (TP + FP) is the proportion of true positives of those that are predicted positives.

- *False positive rate* = FP / (FP + TN) is the proportion of true negatives that are incorrectly predicted positive.

- *False negative rate* = FN / (FN + TP) is the proportion of true positives that are incorrectly predicted negative.

We can illustrate the method for determining the misclassification rate for a classification algorithm using a very simple scenario. Let's say we have two vectors, one containing the predicted classes for a multi-class classifier and the other containing the actual values. In other words, our model uses a categorical response variable with three possible classes. We shall create a simulated data set using the `sample()` function, once for the predicted values `y_hat` and again for the actual values `y`. Then we'll display a confusion matrix comparing the predicted and actual values. The correctly classified values appear along the diagonal of the matrix, whereas the incorrectly classified values appear off the diagonal. It is simple to calculate the misclassification rate by using the formula `1-sum(diag(cm))/sum(cm)`, which sums the diagonal, divides by the sum of all elements of the matrix, and then subtracts from 1 for a value of 0.58. This would be considered a bad misclassification rate, but considering that we're using a simulated, random data set, it is not surprising.

```
> y_hat <- sample(0:2,50,replace=TRUE)
> y <- sample(0:2,50,replace=TRUE)
> cm <- table(y_hat,y)   # Show confusion matrix
> cm
```

```
        y
y_hat  0  1  2
    0  6  4  4
    1  4 11  5
    2  8  4  4
> misclassification_error_rate <- 1-sum(diag(cm))/sum(cm)
> misclassification_error_rate
[1] 0.58
```

Now let's turn our attention to another example of weighing the performance of a classification algorithm, this time using a real data set. One popular source of data sets for use with machine learning is the *UC Irvine Machine Learning Repository*. This resource has many data sets that you can download for experimenting with various statistical learning algorithms. We'll use the Wine Quality data set that contains 11 predictors plus one response variable quality. The response variable is a categorical variable, with a range of values from 3 to 8. The data set has 1,599 observations (wines).

The R code below uses the Random Forest algorithm to classify the wines in terms of quality, and we'd like to measure the accuracy of the model by calculating the misclassification rate. First, we load the randomForest library and then download the data set (as a CSV file) into the current workspace. Then we read the CSV into a data frame df. We also convert quality from integer to factor.

```
> library(randomForest)
> download.file("http://archive.ics.uci.edu/ml/machine-learning-
    databases/wine-quality/winequality-red.csv", "wine.csv")
> df <- read.csv("wine.csv", sep=";", header=TRUE)
> df$quality <- factor(df$quality)
```

We now split the data set into a training set consisting of 70% of the records (1,119 observations), and a test set with 30% (480 observations) - wine_train and wine_test respectively.

```
> n <- nrow(df)
> ntrain <- round(n*0.7)
```

```
> set.seed(333)
> tindex <- sample(n, ntrain)
> wine_train <- df[tindex,] # Create training set
> wine_test <- df[-tindex,] # Create test set
```

Lastly, we use the `randomForest()` algorithm with the training set to fit a model called `rf`. The confusion matrix calculated using the `table()` function uses the actual test set response values, along with the predicted values using the fitted model `rf`. Finally, as in the earlier example, we calculate the misclassification error rate, 0.3604167. A 36% error rate isn't that great, and your task is to minimize this as much as possible. In the next section we'll take a look at cross validation techniques that may help increase the accuracy of the classifier.

```
> rf <- randomForest(quality ~ ., data=wine_train, ntree=20,
      nodesize=5, mtry=9)
> table(wine_test$quality, predict(rf, wine_test))
     3   4   5   6   7   8
3    0   1   2   2   0   0
4    0   2  11   8   1   0
5    0   2 159  35   7   0
6    0   0  45 114  24   1
7    0   0   5  20  34   1
8    0   0   0   2   4   0
> sum(wine_test$quality!=predict(rf, wine_test)) / nrow(wine_test)
[1] 0.3604167
```

CROSS VALIDATION

In previous sections of this chapter, we've seen distinctions between the test error rate (out of sample error) and the training error rate (in sample error). The test error is the average error resulting from using a machine learning algorithm to predict the response on a new observation, i.e., an observation that was not used to train the model. A data scientist can justify the use of a particular algorithm if it results in a low test error. The test error can be easily calculated if a test set is made available. In contrast, the training error can be easily calculated by applying the algorithm to the observations used during the process of training. However, the training error rate often is quite different from the test error rate; more specifically, the training error rate can drastically underestimate the test error rate. We've seen that just because a learning algorithm fits a training set well doesn't mean it is a good model since overfitting may occur. This is why the training set error is not always a good predictor for how well the model will generalize on new observations not seen in the training set.

The process of *cross validation* can be used to directly estimate the test error rate using available training data. Cross validation is a class of methods that estimate the test error rate by *holding out* a subset of the training observations from the fitting process and then applying the algorithm to those held out observations. Cross validation involves repeatedly drawing samples from a training set and refitting a statistical learning model on each sample in order to obtain additional insight about the fitted model. This insight would not be available from fitting the model only once using the original training set. Cross validation is also known as a resampling method.

To illustrate these concepts, let's consider the model selection problem. For example, in the case of polynomial regression we try to choose the degree of polynomial to fit the data: a linear function (degree 1), quadratic function (degree 2), cubic function (degree 3), etc. Essentially we try to select all the coefficients in the polynomial equations plus one more parameter, the degree of the polynomial. Further, let's say we want to choose a model (i.e., degree of polynomial), fit that model, and also get some estimate of how well our fitted model will generalize to new observations. Next, we would work to find the coefficients for each of the proposed polynomials fitted to the training set. Then we'd compute the test error rate for each set of coefficients. In terms of R, this would simply mean using the trained model for each unique formula on the test set and computing the test error rate since the test set is labeled. This would measure the performance of each model on the test set. We would want to look for the lowest test error rate in order to choose the "best" model, i.e., the model with the best possible performance on the test set. Unfortunately, this is not a fair estimate of generalization because it is an optimistic estimate of the generalization error. Since we fit the polynomial degree parameter to the test set, it would likely do better on this test set than it would on new observations.

To address this problem, let's go back to the model selection step. Instead of splitting the data set into training and test, we split it into three pieces. The first piece is the *training set* as usual, the second piece is called the *cross validation set*, and the last piece is called the *test set*. The typical ratio to split the pieces is 60% for training, 20% for cross validation and 20% for test (although some data scientists use a 50%, 25%, 25% split). Each of these data sets also will have their own associated errors: *training error rate, cross validation error rate*, and *test error rate*.

Now let's return to the problem we described above where using the test error rate on the various model options did not yield a fair estimate of how well the winning model would generalize on new data. Instead, we'll use the cross validation set to select the model. In R, the process would be as follows:

- Fit a linear model based on each of the proposed polynomial functions. If we had polynomials from degree 1 up to degree 5, we'd fit five linear models each based on the training set.

- Test each of the five models on the cross validation set to see how well each one does. We would calculate the cross validation error rate for each.

- Pick the model with the lowest cross validation error rate. Say you determine the cubic polynomial (of degree 3) has the lowest cross validation error. Here, we have fit the polynomial degree 3 to the cross validation set. This means the degree of polynomial is no longer fit to the test set.

- Now we can use the remaining test set to estimate the generalization error of the model.

Revisiting the bias-variance tradeoff issue while now considering cross validation, we can observe that high bias (underfit) occurs when the training error rate is high and the cross validation error is also high, i.e., the cross validation error might be close to or even a bit higher than the training error rate. In contrast, high variance (overfit) occurs when the training error rate is low, i.e., you're fitting the training set very well but the cross validation error will be much larger.

In continuing with the theme outlined in the example above, accuracy on the training set (also known as resubstitution accuracy) is often optimistic in that we're trying a collection of different models and selecting the best one on the training set. This selection will always be tuned to the quirks of the training set and may not be the accurate representation of what that prediction accuracy would be on a new sample.

A better estimate comes from an independent data set—say, test set accuracy. But there's a problem with this because if we repeatedly use the test set to evaluate the out of sample accuracy of the model, then in a sense the test set has become part of the training set and we still don't have an outside measure, i.e., an independent evaluation of the test set error.

To estimate the test set accuracy, we need to use something about the training set in order to get a good estimate of the test set accuracy, so we can build our models entirely using the training set and only evaluate once on the test set. The way data scientists achieve this accuracy measure is with cross validation. The conceptual approach is outlined here:

- Take the training set and split it into two pieces, which we can view as a smaller training set and a test set (cross validation set).

- Build a model based on the training set (a subset of our original training set).

- Evaluate the model based on the test set (a subset of our original training set, also known as the cross validation set).

- Repeat this process a number of times and average the estimated errors.

This process can be used for choosing feature variables to include in the model. We can fit a number of models with a selected number of feature variables included and then use the ones that fit best on the cross validation test sets. We can also choose the specific type of algorithm to use and elect the one that does best on the cross validation test sets. We also can choose the tuning parameters for the predictive models. Through all this, we leave the original test set completely alone since it is never used in this process. So when we finally apply our prediction algorithm to the test set, it will be an unbiased measurement of the out of sample accuracy.

There are several different resampling methods for creating the cross validation sets. In general these methods for estimating model performance operate similarly; a subset of samples is used to fit a model, and the remaining samples are used to estimate the efficiency of the models. This process is repeated multiple times, and the results are aggregated and summarized. The differences in the methods outlined below center on the way in which subsamples are chosen.

- **Random subsampling**: With this method, we use a random sampling of the original training set to divide it into two parts: a training set and a cross validation set (or hold-out set). The new training set will be larger than the new cross validation set. Once you create a split, you'd use the new training set and build a model. Then you would apply the model to predict the cross validation set and evaluate the accuracy. The resulting cross validation set error rate (MSE for a quantitative response) provides an estimate of the test error rate. You can repeat this process for a number of different random subsamples and then average the errors.

- **K-fold cross validation**: Here we randomly divide the original training set into k equal sized groups for cross validation. The choice of k is usually 5 or 10, but there is no hard and fast rule. For example, say k is chosen to be 3. Here you'd split the original training set into three equal sized pieces or folds. The first fold is treated as a cross validation set, and the model is fit on the observations in the remaining k-1 folds. The cross validation error rate is calculated on the observations in the held-out fold. This procedure is repeated k times. For each iteration, a different fold is treated as the cross validation set. This process yields k estimates of the test error. The k-fold cross validation estimate is computed by averaging these values. For k-fold cross validation, the larger the value of k, the less bias and more variance you'll get, while smaller values of k yield more bias and less variance. In this context, the bias is the difference between the estimated and true values of performance. If you take a large k like 20, you'll get a very accurate estimate of the bias between the predicted values and actual values, but it will be highly variable, i.e., it will depend a lot on the specific subsets you take. For smaller k values, you won't necessarily get as good an estimate of the out of sample error rate because you're only leaving one sample out, so you're using most of your data to train your model. But there will be less variance since there are fewer subsets that can make up, say, a 2-fold cross validation.

- **Leave one out cross validation (LOOCV)**: In a manner similar to the random subsampling method, LOOCV involves splitting the set of observations into two parts. We leave out exactly one sample and build a model on all the remaining samples. Then we predict the value of the one sample we left out. We iterate through all the samples in the original training set, leaving one out each time. Since the left out observation was not used in the fitting process, the accuracy method (MSE) provides a roughly unbiased estimate for the out of sample accuracy rate. The LOOCV estimate is the average of the individual test error estimates. We can see that LOOCV is a special case of k-fold cross validation in which k equals the number of observations. LOOCV has far less bias than the random subsampling method. With LOOCV, we repeatedly fit the model using training sets that are nearly as big as the entire data set (one observation held out). In contrast, the random subsampling approach uses a training set typically around half the size of the original data set. This means that the LOOCV approach tends not to overestimate the test error rate as much as the random subsampling approach.

Note that the random sampling done with cross validation must be done *without replacement* since we are subsampling the data sets. Also, if you use cross validation to choose predictors, you must estimate errors on an independent data set in order to get a true out of sample value. Essentially this means that if you use cross validation to select your model, the cross validation error rates will not necessarily be a good representation of the real out of sample error rate since you'll always pick the best model. Again, the best way to achieve good performance is to apply your model just one time with an independent test set.

Let's take a look at a comprehensive example that uses cross validation to perform model selection from comparison of estimate test error rates. In order to facilitate the cross validation process, we'll use the `errorest()` function in the R `ipred` package. This function use a 10-fold cross validation to estimate the test error of any given model. In the R code below, we'll use `errorest()` on a series of familiar algorithms. We start by installing and loading `ipred` (improved predictors) and setting the seed value for reproducible results.

```
> install.packages("ipred")
> library(ipred)
> set.seed(314)
```

For our test scenarios, we'll use the `iris` data set along with `errorest()` for random forest, naïve Bayes, K-nearest neighbor, support vector machines, and linear discriminant analysis. The `errorest()` function requires a formula, data set, and model. It also requires a predict function that returns a predicted class. The return of `errorest()` is a single estimate test error from the cross validation.

```
> # Random forest algorithm
> library(randomForest)
> cv_error <- errorest(Species~., data=iris, model=randomForest)
> cv_error$error   # class=cvclass
[1] 0.04666667
> # Naive Bayes algorithm
> library(e1071)
> predict_nb <- function(object, newdata) {
  predict(object, newdata[,-1])
}
> cv_error <- errorest(Species~., data=iris, model=naiveBayes,
    predict=predict_nb)
> cv_error$error
[1] 0.04666667
> # K-nearest neighbor
> library(class)
```

```
> predict_knn <- function(object, newdata){
  predict.ipredknn(object, newdata, type="class")
}
> cv_error <- errorest(Species~., data=iris, model=ipredknn,
    predict=predict_knn) # default k=5
> cv_error$error
[1] 0.03333333
> # Support vector machines
> library(e1071)
> cv_error <- errorest(Species~., data=iris, model=svm)
> cv_error$error
[1] 0.03333333
> # Linear Discriminant Analysis
> library(MASS)
> predict_lda <- function(object, newdata){
  predict(object, newdata)$class
}
> cv_error <- errorest(Species~., data=iris, model=lda,
    predict=predict_lda)
> cv_error$error
[1] 0.02
```

After running through all the candidate algorithms, we can examine the cross validation errors and select the best one. Here is a summary of the results of our experiment:

Algorithm	10-fold CV Error
Random Forest	0.04666667
Naïve Bayes	0.04666667
K-nearest Neighbor	0.03333333
Support Vector Machines	0.03333333
Linear Discriminant Analysis	0.02

Table 7-1 CV error analysis across a series of common algorithms

As we can see by the results, many models are more or less equivalent in terms of predictive performance while we seek the lowest CV error value. The linear discriminant analysis (LDA) algorithm appears to be a good choice. Suppose we choose LDA as the winning model. We can derive the standard deviation of its cross validation error by repeating the 10-fold cross validation 25 times.

```
> set.seed(314)
> cv_result <- replicate(25, errorest(Species~., data=iris,
    model=lda, predict=predict_lda)$error)
> cv_result  # Numeric vector, length=25
> sd(cv_result)
[1] 0
```

We get zero spread, so the cross validation error should be very close to the true test error. Various summary and graphical methods are available to assess the selected model. For categorical response, we can display the prediction performance via a confusion matrix using the out of sample predictions from the cross validation process.

```
> pred_species <- errorest(Species~., data=iris, model=lda,
    predict=predict_lda,
    est.para=control.errorest(predictions=TRUE))$predictions

> table(iris$Species, pred_species)  # confusion matrix
           pred_species
           setosa versicolor virginica
setosa       50        0         0
versicolor    0       48         2
virginica     0        1        49
```

OTHER MACHINE LEARNING DIAGNOSTICS

The last topic we'll consider in this chapter of evaluating model performance is a basic set of diagnostic guidelines to follow when your attempt at generalizing your algorithm to new data not in the training set yields unacceptably large errors in prediction. A diagnostic is a test that you can run to gain insight into what is and what is not working with a machine learning algorithm and gain guidance as to how best improve its performance. Diagnostics take time to implement, but doing so can be a very good use of your time.

Unfortunately, many times the strategy of choice tends to be ordinary "gut feeling" by randomly picking one of the strategies below. This can lead the data scientist down multiple fruitless avenues that ultimately are wastes of time. A more structured, organized, and thoughtful approach is usually more productive.

GET MORE TRAINING OBSERVATIONS

This strategy is probably the simplest: Whenever in doubt about your algorithm's predictive power, try to get more data. An old maxim in data science is "more data always trumps a clever algorithm." Although not always a hard and fast rule, this means that you often can improve the accuracy of your algorithm by expanding the data set upon which it operates. So with this strategy, you can imagine trying to seek out more data by conducting additional surveys, for example.

In practice, a data scientist might spend a lot of time obtaining, say, ten times as much training data, but as it turns out the additional data doesn't actually help. This means we can't approach this data gathering technique for expanding predictive power blindly. When collecting more data results in more time and cost for the project, we need to carefully assess the situation before spending a lot of effort. A pragmatic approach is to plot the error against the size of data. Essentially we sample different sizes of training sets with different models and plot both the cross validation error and the training error rate with respect to the training set size. With this insight, we can better determine whether more data leads to lower error rates.

FEATURE REDUCTION

When the number of feature variables is large, you may wish to engage the process of feature engineering (an early part of the data science process) again in order to reduce the number of variables your model uses for the purpose of prediction. Spending time to find a smaller subset of the feature variables can help avoid overfitting.

FEATURE ADDITION

Although not immediately intuitive, finding new feature variables that were not previously considered (and maybe not available earlier) can serve to enhance the predictive power of your model. Maybe the current set of features are not informative enough, so you collect different data, possibly through more directed surveys, that can add clarity to the predictive process. Unfortunately, this process could become a huge project, and there's no concrete way to determine up front whether spending this time will actually help.

ADD POLYNOMIAL FEATURES

You might try adding more terms to polynomials used for regression problems, such as adding more n^{th} order terms for certain features, or product terms for groups of features that could increase the model's performance. Again, spending time on an orderly approach for adding polynomial terms may or may not prove successful.

FINE TUNING THE REGULARIZATION PARAMETER

You can also experiment with increasing and decreasing the regularization parameter *lambda* to see what effect it has on the algorithm's performance. This strategy is relatively simple since it involves changing a single argument in an R function call.

SUMMARY

Supervised machine learning works to makes predictions for continuous response variables as we saw in Chapter 5 and also categorical response variables as we saw in Chapter 6. In this chapter we attempted gauge the accuracy of these statistical learning models and also examined a variety of methods for improving this accuracy.

Here is a summary of what you've learned in this chapter:

- We highlighted the most common problem with machine learning including overfitting, where an algorithm is trained too well for accuracy with a specific training data set.

- We also reviewed the concepts of bias and variance, and how to take strides in balancing the two with a detailed understanding of the bias-variance tradeoff.

- We examined the thorny effects of confounding variables, where a variable is correlated with both the response variable and the predictor variables.

- We learned about data leakage, a tough-to-detect situation where the data you are using to train a machine learning algorithm happens to have the information you are trying to predict.

- We defined methods for calculating metrics for determining the accuracy of regression models.

- We defined methods for calculating metrics for determining the accuracy of classification models.

- We determined how the process of cross validation serves to reduce the generalization error rate of a statistical learning model.

- We finished the chapter by offering up a handful of additional techniques to use when predictive performance is lacking.

Chapter 8
Unsupervised Learning

In previous chapters, we've seen a number of machine learning techniques under the umbrella of supervised learning such as regression and classification. These techniques have used labeled training data sets comprised of feature variables measured on a collection of observations to make predictions with new test data sets. In this chapter, we'll look at an entirely new type of machine learning: *unsupervised learning*. Although not nearly as common as supervised learning, this new methodology provides great potential for discovering previously unknown insights from existing *unlabeled* data sets. This means the data sets used for unsupervised learning do not contain a response variable, since we're not trying to predict anything. The main use of unsupervised learning is to discover unknown patterns within data, e.g., grouping similar data or detecting outliers. Identifying clusters is a classical scenario of unsupervised learning.

Unsupervised refers to the fact that we're trying to understand the structure of our underlying data rather than trying to optimize for a specific, pre-labeled criterion (such as creating a predictive model). Unsupervised learning is a great technique for exploratory analysis (as covered in Chapter 4), but it tends to be more subjective since there is no specific goal like the prediction of a response variable. It is also difficult to assess the result obtained from unsupervised learning methods because there are no universally accepted procedures for evaluating model performance or validating results on an independent data set. The whole premise behind supervised learning is such that you can verify your work by seeing how well your model predicts the response variable on test data sets not used in training the model. But with unsupervised learning, there is no way to verify your work because there is no right answer. This is why it is called unsupervised learning.

As the expanse of big data continues to grow in volume, variety, and velocity, unsupervised learning techniques are also growing in importance in many application areas. For example, an e-commerce website can identify groups of customers with similar browsing and purchase histories, as well as products that are of particular interest to the customers within each group. In general, any time you can effectively group individuals with similar demographics, behavior, and/or preferences means you can be more successful in providing a targeted marketing effort to increase sales.

CLUSTERING

The primary method of unsupervised learning is called clustering, a very broad set of techniques used for identifying groups, or clusters, of values in a data set. Clustering organizes things that are "close" and places them into groups. There are a number of things to consider when using clustering:

- How do we define "close" when we talk about data measurements?

- How do we group things once we've defined "close"?

- How do we visualize the grouping?

- How do we interpret the groupings created from this statistical process that might be hard to believe or were just created due to noise?

Let's begin by discussing how we define closeness, which is the most important step in a clustering algorithm. The distance metric must be appropriate to the kind of data you have. If not, then you can expect to get clusters that are less easy to interpret, i.e., the patterns are less clearly represented. For continuous variables, you can use Euclidean distance, or instead of looking at the smallest distance, you can look at the greatest similarity or binary measures of distance such as the Manhattan distance. The choice of distance or similarity measure is very important to the problem you're analyzing in order to get good clustering results.

First, we'll consider *Euclidean* distance. It will be useful to visualize this metric with Figure 8-1 showing how to look at the distance between New York City and Boston. As labeled on the graph, the y-coordinates measure the latitude values for both cities, and the x-coordinates measure longitude. Further, $y1-y2$ is the difference between latitudes, and $x1-x2$ is the difference between the longitudes. What we're looking to define is some combination of these two differences to measure the distance between NYC and Boston. If you recall from basic geometry, this is just the Pythagorean Theorem with the formula shown. Of course, this distance measure is for two dimensions. We can generalize the formula for many dimensions representing feature variables contributing to the clustering problem. We'll arbitrarily use the letters A – Z to represent these variables in the generalized formula shown in the figure. This distance measure is used with quantitative (continuous) variables when performing clustering. The problem with trying to visualize clusters in more than three dimensions is that there is no way to represent such an organization. This is where dimensionality reduction comes in handy, where you can create a new data set with fewer feature variables that is roughly equivalent to the original. We'll discuss this technique later in this chapter.

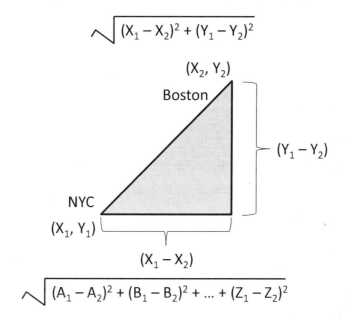

Figure 8-1 Example of calculating Euclidean distance

Another metric for calculating distance is called the *Manhattan* distance, which often is used for binary variables. As depicted in Figure 8-2, think of the labeled points on the graph, A and B, as buildings in a big city. Any of the three groups of line segments have the same distance in terms of number of blocks traveled. The formula for Manhattan distance is shown in the graph. It looks similar to Euclidean distance, but instead of taking the square root of the sum of the differences between coordinates, you just take the sum of the absolute values of the differences between coordinates.

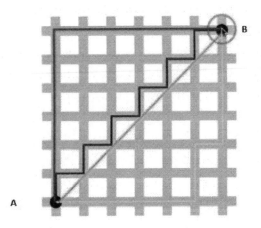

In general:

$$|A_1 - A_2| + |B_1 - B_2| + \ldots + |Z_1 - Z_2|$$

Figure 8-2 Example of calculating Manhattan distance (https://en.wikipedia.org/wiki/Taxicab_geometry)

SIMULATING CLUSTERS

In order to visualize how data can be grouped into clusters, we will start with an example using a small simulated data set. R is very good at allowing us to generate simulated data for use with statistical techniques. In this example, we'll use the rnorm() function to supply the data items.

```
> set.seed(1234) # Set seed to get same data set each time
> par(mar=c(0,0,0,0)) # Set plot margins
> # Define numeric vector, length=12
> # vector of means: 1 1 1 1 2 2 2 2 3 3 3 3
> x <- rnorm(12, mean=rep(1:3, each=4), sd=0.2)
> # Define numeric vector, length=12
> # vector of means: 1 1 1 1 2 2 2 2 1 1 1 1
> y <- rnorm(12, mean=rep(c(1,2,1), each=4), sd=0.2)
> # x and y coordinates to create 3 clusters
> plot(x,y, col="dark green", pch=19, cex=3)
> # Display integer labels to the upper-right of the dot
```

```
> text(x+0.05, y+0.05, labels=as.character(1:12))
```

The above code generates two vectors, x and y, that are used as coordinates for the plot. Note that we used the rnorm() function in such a way so as to create three clusters. The way we did that was by using the mean parameter, along with the sd parameter, to make sure the ordered pairs are roughly grouped together forming clusters. The resulting plot is shown in Figure 8-3. You can easily pick out the clusters; I've manually drawn red ellipses around each cluster. Please experiment with changing the x and y vectors using different mean and sd parameters to see that the distribution of points does not always make the clusters so recognizable.

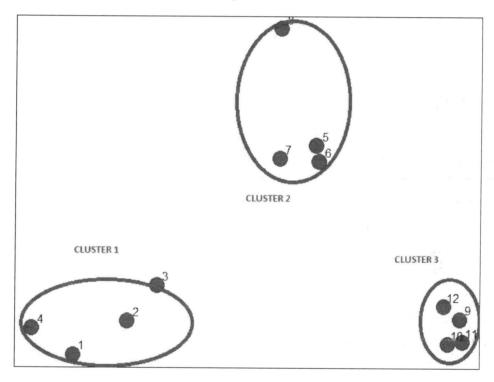

Figure 8-3 Cluster plot using a simulated data set showing relationship between data values

HIERARCHICAL CLUSTERING

The hierarchical clustering algorithm compares all pairs of data points and then merges the pairs with the closest distance. The hclust() function in the stats package implements hierarchical clustering in R. To perform hierarchical clustering, we require a defined distance measure and a method for merging two observations. We'll use Euclidean distance as the dissimilarity measure.

The algorithm proceeds in the following manner:

1. Compute the distance between every pair of points/clusters. Computing the distance between point A and point B is done via the distance function. Computing the distance between point A and cluster B may first compute distance of all point pairs (one from cluster A and the other from cluster B) and then pick either min/max/avg of these pairs.

2. Combine the two closest point/pairs into a cluster. Repeat step 1 until only one big cluster remains.

Hierarchical clustering is an agglomerative (bottom-up) approach toward the clustering process. You find the closest two observations or variables, merge them together into a single super observation, and then, using the rest of the observations plus the two you merged together, find the next closest two observations. This process continues until you've merged all the observations together into one big object. Since its complexity is high, hierarchical clustering is typically used when the number of points is not too large.

It is useful to visualize the hierarchical clustering process by examining the first couple of steps. The visualization for hierarchical clustering is a tree structure plot called a *dendrogram*. Based on the cluster diagram above, we'll start by identifying the two closest points (5 and 6 on the plot). These two points will be merged by averaging their x and y values. In parallel, the resulting dendrogram will have the first two branches for points 5 and 6. Next, we look for the second two closest points and find points 10 and 11, which are merged too. The resulting dendrogram will have another two branches for points 10 and 11. You keep going like this, identifying the next two closest points (which can also be merged points), merging as you go. The final dendrogram is shown in Figure 8-6. Note that the lowest level branches are for the first two sets of closest points, 5 and 6, along with 10 and 11. We see that the merge point from 10 and 11 was eventually merged with the merged points 9 and 12. Eventually, all of the points were merged at the very top of the dendrogram. The goal of the dendrogram is to group points in the plot whose distance determined they were close together. For example, points 5, 6, 7, and 8 were all close together. Further, points 1, 2, 3, and 4 were close together, and points 9, 10, 11, and 12 were all close together. This corresponds to the visual inspection we did in Figure 8-4.

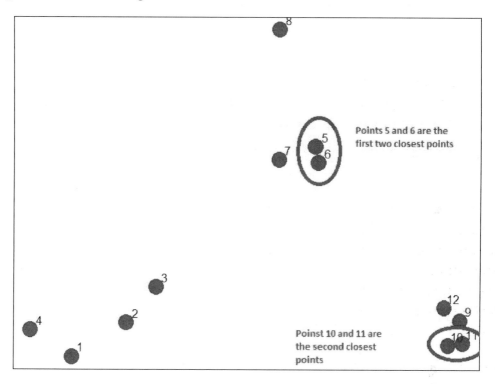

Figure 8-4 Hierarchical clustering process

Let's continue using the simulated data set from the previous section. First, we'll load the x and y values into a data frame. Then we'll use the dist() function to calculate the Euclidean distance. Note: In addition to Manhattan distance, there are several other special purpose distance measures.

```
> dataFrame <- data.frame(x=x, y=y)   # 12x2 data frame
# Calculate distance between 12 points observed
# (distance between columns)
> distxy <- dist(df)    # Default distance method=Euclidean
#distxy <- dist(df, method="minkowski")   # Class=dist!!
# Produce cluster object. hclust() requires a dist object
```

```
# Returns a hclust object
> hClustering <- hclust(distxy, method="complete")
# Plot dendrogram showing 3 clusters
> plot(hClustering)
> cutree(hClustering,h=1.5)     # Will yield fewer clusters
[1] 1 1 1 1 2 2 2 2 3 3 3 3
> cutree(hClustering,h=0.5)     # Will yield more clusters
[1] 1 2 2 1 3 3 3 4 5 5 5 5
```

Figure 8-5 shows the results for the dist() function, calculating the distance between each point in the data frame. For example, the distance between point 1 and point 2 is 0.34, the distance between point 1 and point 3 is 0.57, etc. The top part of the rectangle of values is not included since it will be the same as the bottom part. In addition, the diagonal of the matrix is not shown since the distance between any point and itself is always zero.

```
> dist(df)
            1          2          3          4          5          6          7          8          9         10         11
2  0.34120511
3  0.57493739 0.24102750
4  0.26381786 0.52578819 0.71861759
5  1.69424700 1.35818182 1.11952883 1.80666768
6  1.65812902 1.31960442 1.08338841 1.78081321 0.08150268
7  1.49823399 1.16620981 0.92568723 1.60131659 0.21110433 0.21666557
8  1.99149025 1.69093111 1.45648906 2.02849490 0.61704200 0.69791931 0.65062566
9  2.13629539 1.83167669 1.67835968 2.35675598 1.18349654 1.11500116 1.28582631 1.76460709
10 2.06419586 1.76999236 1.63109790 2.29239480 1.23847877 1.16550201 1.32063059 1.83517785 0.14090406
11 2.14702468 1.85183204 1.71074417 2.37461984 1.28153948 1.21077373 1.37369662 1.86999431 0.11624471 0.08317570
12 2.05664233 1.74662555 1.58658782 2.27232243 1.07700974 1.00777231 1.17740375 1.66223814 0.10848966 0.19128645 0.20802789
```

Figure 8-5 Output from the dist() function

The hclust() function performs the actual hierarchical clustering. The function takes a dist object and, optionally, a parameter indicating the linkage method to be used. The default method is called complete, but there are also average and single. The complete linkage method compares the points that are farthest apart (maximal dissimilarity) before it does the clustering. Conversely, the single method uses minimal intercluster dissimilarity. Alternatively, the average method takes the average of groups of points that are close together (i.e., it calculates the average x and y coordinates), merges them to yield new points, and then compares the distance between the new points to get the distance between the clusters. Depending on the linkage method, you'll get widely different clustering diagrams. Average and complete linkage tend to yield more balanced clusters. The trick is to use different linkage methods to yield dendrograms that you can consider to see which clusters make sense to the problem domain.

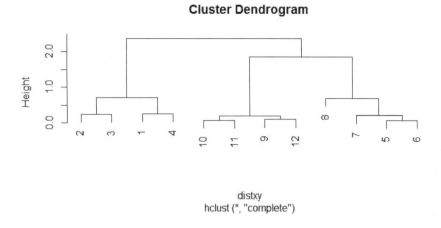

Figure 8-6 Cluster dendrogram for simulated data set

In order to decide which cluster a point is in, you have to cut the dendrogram tree at some point. Cutting the tree with hierarchical clustering is done with the `cutree()` function. If we cut the tree somewhere between height 1.0 and 1.5 or so, we get three clusters, as indicated in Figure 8-7.

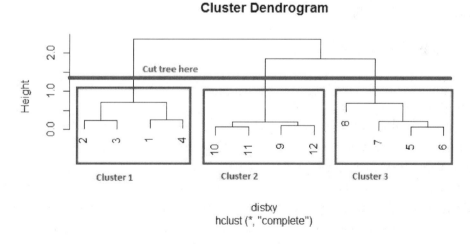

Figure 8-7 Cutting the dendrogram tree high yields fewer clusters

Now if, instead, we cut the tree at 0.5, we would end up with more clusters. Figure 8-8 shows the result of the lower height cutting. The idea with various cutting points is that hierarchical clustering requires you to carefully review each cut height and the resulting clusters in terms of whether it makes sense for the problem domain being analyzed. Some heights yield clusters that provide good insight into the data, while other clusters might be nonsensical. Working with a domain expert at this stage in the analysis is critical.

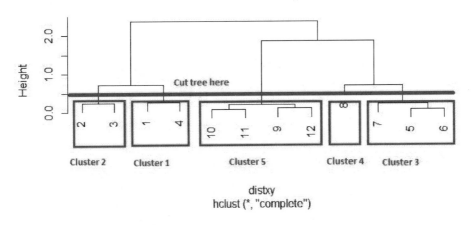

Figure 8-8 Cutting the dendrogram tree low yields more clusters

Another way to evaluate hierarchical clusters is to consider the quantitative data after it has been clustered using a heat map. The `heatmap()` function clusters the rows and columns of the data matrix. The heat map uses the hierarchical clustering algorithm to cluster the rows and columns and draw dendrograms for each axis. In this case, the clustering of the columns is not very interesting because there are just two variables, x and y. But the observation of those variables (the rows) yields interesting clusters. A heat map allows you to see patterns in the quantitative data.

```
> set.seed(143)
> dataMatrix <- as.matrix(dataFrame)[sample(1:12),]  # 12x2
> heatmap(dataMatrix)
```

Now let's consider another example of hierarchical clustering using a non-simulated data set, the familiar `iris` data set. In the code below, we'll take a random sample of 40 observations, use Euclidean distance to compute a distance matrix, use the average linkage method to compute the clusters, and then plot the resulting dendrogram, shown in Figure 8-9. Notice how we use labels based on the `Species` variable to denote the clusters obtained.

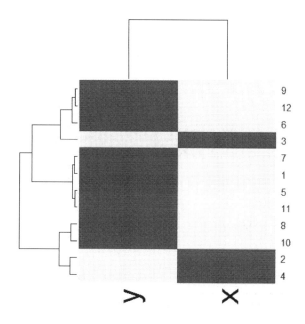

Figure 8-9 Heat map of variables x and y with dendrograms on each axis

As we move up the tree in the `iris` dendrogram, some leaves begin to merge into branches. These correspond to observations that are similar to each other. The earlier (lower in the tree) merges occur, the more similar the groups of observations are to each other. On the other hand, observations that merge later (near the top of the tree) can be quite different. More precisely, for any two observations, we can look for the point in the tree where branches containing those two observations are first merged. The height of this merge indicates how different the two observations are. Thus, observations that merge at the very bottom of the tree are quite similar to each other, whereas observations that merge close to the top of the tree will tend to be quite different. In general, we can draw conclusions about the similarity of two observations based on the location on the vertical axis of the dendrogram (but not the horizontal axis) where branches containing those two observations first merged.

Cutting the dendrogram at different vertical heights will yield different clusters. In practice, you can look at the dendrogram and select a sensible number of clusters by eye based on the heights of the merge and the number of clusters desired. In the case of the `iris` data set, we can cut the tree at a place to yield four clusters.

The code below will generated a plot rendering a cluster dendrogram for the `iris` data set, as shown in Figure 8-10.

```
> data(iris)
> # Get a sample from the iris data set
> # Randomly choose 40 observations from iris
> iris_sample <- iris[sample(1:150, 40),]
> distance_metric <- dist(iris_sample[,-5], method="euclidean") > #
    dist object
> # Using hclust() from stats package using "average" cluster
> cluster <- hclust(distance_metric, method="average")
> # Plot the cluster dendrogram
> plot(cluster, hang=-1, label=iris_sample$Species, main="Iris Data
    Set Clusters")
```

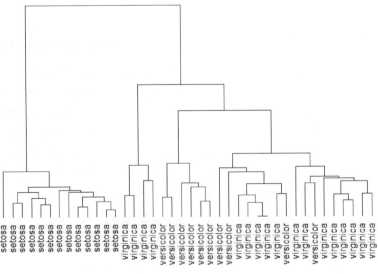

Figure 8-10 Cluster dendrogram for `iris` dataset

Let's summarize some key points about what you can expect from hierarchical clustering. It provides ideas about the relationships between variables and observations, but the picture may be unstable in the following ways:

- If you change a few data points, leave a few data points out, or find some of the data points have missing values, you may get dramatically different clusterings. This is because the distance metric changes relative to other data points.
- The picture changes if you have different missing values in your data set.
- The picture changes if you pick a different distance metric.
- The picture changes if you pick a different linkage (merging) strategy.
- The picture changes if you scale of points for one variable. If you standardize one set of points but not the others, then you get very different clustering results.

Hierarchical clustering is a deterministic algorithm in the sense that using the same data points, the same distance metric, and the same merging strategy will yield the same dendrogram. Furthermore, choosing where to cut the tree is not always obvious. Hierarchical clustering is more useful for visual exploration rather than confirmatory analysis.

K-MEANS CLUSTERING

Now let's turn our attention to another important unsupervised machine learning algorithm: K-means clustering. K-means clustering is different from hierarchical clustering in that it is a partitioning approach as opposed to an agglomerative approach. A partitioning approach starts with all of the data points and tries to divide them into a fixed number of clusters. K-means is applied to a set of quantitative variables. The number of clusters is fixed in advance, and then we must guess where the centers (called "centroids") of those clusters might be. Next we assign points to the closest centroid and then recalculate the centroids to iterate through this clustering approach.

The requirements for K-means clustering are as follows:

- A defined distance metric. The primary distance metric used in K-means clustering is Euclidean distance.
- Choosing the number of clusters in advance. You often start with a large number of clusters picked by intuition, apply K-means clustering, look at the clusters to see if they seem reasonable, and then reduce the number of clusters.
- An initial guess for the cluster centroids.

At the end of K-means clustering, you obtain the final estimate of the cluster centers (centroids) and an assignment of each data point to each of the clusters. You should note that K-means is not deterministic; i.e., a different starting number of clusters will yield a different number of iterations in the algorithm. To illustrate this process, let's go back to the same simulated 12-point data set we used for hierarchical clustering to see how the K-means clustering algorithm works. Let's say that we're interested in three clusters, as before, and provide an initial guess (chosen to illustrate how the process works) for the cluster centroids (points with a crosshatch symbol in the figure). Figure 8-11 shows our starting point for the K-means algorithm.

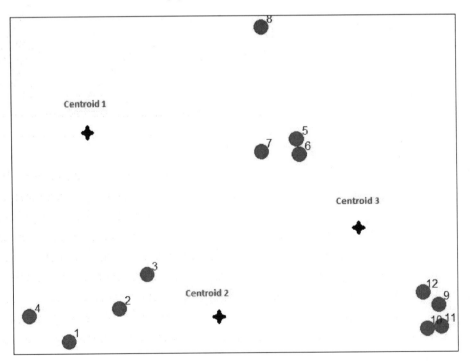

Figure 8-11 K-means clustering starting point with centroid guesses

Now we need to assign all of the points to the closest centroid in Euclidean distance. So the clusters of points we obtain with this process are as follows: the points (4, 8) are closest to centroid 1, the points (1, 2, 3) are closest to centroid 2, and the points (5, 6, 7, 9, 10, 11, 12) are closest to centroid 3. Figure 8-12 shows the resulting clusters.

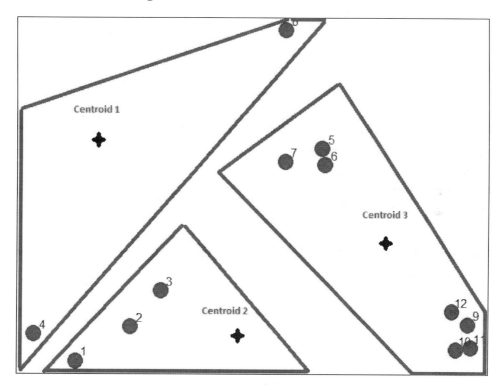

Figure 8-12 K-means clustering first step: assigning clusters

The next step in the K-means algorithm is to recalculate the centroids. So we take the average x-value and average y-value of the points (4, 8) and get a new center for cluster 1. Likewise, we take the x and y average values for points, (1, 2, 3) and get a new centroid 2. Finally, we perform that same recalculation for centroid 3. Then we can recalculate the distance to each centroid from each of the points and re-assign points to the appropriate centroids. You continue to iterate this procedure by updating the centroids again. You'll notice that the centroids move to align themselves with specific clusters. After applying the K-means clustering algorithm, the final set of clusters shown in Figure 8-13 will be determined.

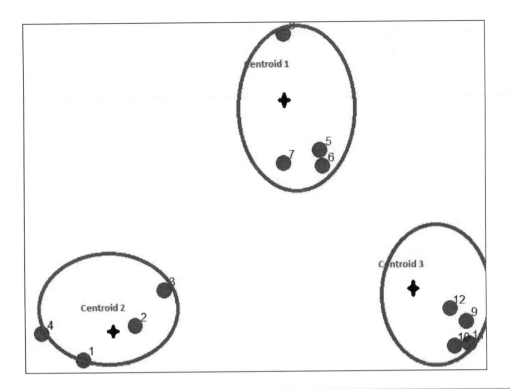

Figure 8-13 Clusters that result from performing K-means algorithm

K-means clustering can be performed in R using the kmeans() function that is found in the base stats package. In this case, we'll pass the function a data frame containing the data points for the observations we'll be clustering, along with the number of centers we'd like to consider, using the centers argument (locations chosen randomly). Alternatively, we could have passed in the centers argument, a matrix containing the x and y coordinates for the cluster centers. We can also pass the number of iterations to perform and the maximum iterations with the iter.max argument, so if the algorithm is not converging, you may end up with excessive K-means processing time, especially for large data sets. The default value for iter.max is 10, but you may wish to experiment with higher values. Finally, you can specify the number of "starts" for the algorithm using the nstart argument. Since the algorithm is not deterministic, if you give it the exact same data with different centers values, you may see it converge to a different set of clusters. So with nstart, you can allow the K-means algorithm to restart multiple times to get an average cluster across multiple starts.

Here is some sample code to perform K-means clustering. Notice that we need to set the seed value to get reproducible results each time we run the code because the K-means algorithm uses a random number generator to come up with the centers when you use the `centers` argument.

```
> df <- data.frame(x,y)
> set.seed(1234)
> # Create a kmeans object with initial number of centroids=3
> kmeans1 <- kmeans(df,centers=3, iter.max=10)
> names(kmeans1)
[1] "cluster"   "centers"   "totss"   "withinss"   "tot.withinss"
[6] "betweenss"   "size"   "iter"   "ifault"
> # Show which cluster each data point assigned to
> kmeans1$cluster      # This is an integer vector
[1] 3 3 3 3 1 1 1 1 2 2 2 2
> kmeans1$centers
          x           y
1 1.9906904 2.0078229
2 2.8534966 0.9831222
3 0.8904553 1.0068707
```

We see with `names(kmeans1)` that the `kmeans1` object is returned from the `kmeans()` function including clusters with `kmeans1$cluster`, centers of those clusters with `kmeans1$centers`, and information about how variable the estimates of those clusters are. The `cluster` component of the K-means object indicates which cluster each data point has been assigned to. In this example, the first four data points are assigned to the third cluster, the next four data points to the first cluster, and the last four data points to the second cluster.

Now to plot the clusters, we can use the following code that uses the `cluster` and `centers` components of the K-means object. The resulting plot is shown in Figure 8-14. The crosses on the plot show the centers of each cluster. In general, the delineation of clusters and their centers won't be as clean as this example.

```
> par(mar=rep(0.2,4))
> # Plot the data points using unique colors for each cluster
> plot(x,y,col=kmeans1$cluster,pch=19,cex=2)
> # Draw crosses showing cluster centers
> points(kmeans1$centers,col=1:4,pch=3,cex=3,lwd=3)
```

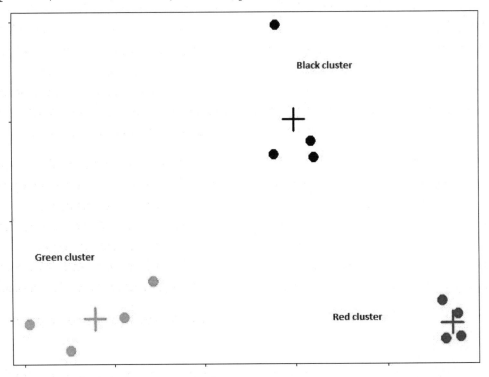

Figure 8-14 Plotting the results of the kmeans() function

PRINCIPAL COMPONENT ANALYSIS

Principal Component Analysis (PCA) is the process by which we can compute *principal components* and use them for better understanding of the data. PCA is considered an unsupervised machine learning method because it involves only a set of feature variables and no associated response variable. PCA also serves as a useful tool for exploratory analysis and data visualization. This section explores the process whereby you can perform PCA on a given data set to obtain increased value.

Let's start by discussing what motivates the need for principal components. Say you have a data set with 12 feature variables. One technique in exploratory data analysis is to examine scatter plots to compare each of the variables against all the others. The problem is that for 12 variables, you'll need 66 plots (the number of combinations of feature variables). If you had 24 variables, the situation would be even more overwhelming. In addition, the information in any one of the plots represents a small fraction of the information in the data set. A better way to approach this problem is to find a lower-dimension representation of the data that captures as much of the information as possible. In the case of the 12 feature variables, we'd like to find a two-dimension representation that contains as much of the *variation* as possible. Then we can plot the observations in this low-dimension space.

PCA is a methodology to make this happen. PCA computes fewer dimensions that represent the most interesting portion of the data. The way it computes principal components is founded in mathematics (linear algebra) and is beyond the scope of this book. Essentially, PCA seeks to transform the original variables to a new set of variables that are (1) linear combinations of the variables in the data set, (2) uncorrelated with each other, and (3) ordered according to the amount of variation of the original variables that they explain.

In the R environment, we have a number of different options for performing PCA. Here is a short list:

- Use the `prcomp()` function in the package `stats`. This function is a numerically stable routine that is the preferred method of computing PCA. It is based on the *singular value decomposition* (SVD) algorithm.

- Use the `princomp()` function, also in the package `stats`. This function is slightly less stable but has more features.

- Use the `svd()` function in the base R package. PCA is based on the singular value decomposition method, and using it requires more mathematics knowledge. It is best to use a function like `prcomp()` that incorporates SVD.

- Calculate PCA "by hand" by calculating the covariance matrix, using it to calculate the eigenvalues and eigenvectors, and then using matrix multiplication to estimate the principal components. This method would be instructional for you to fully understand how PCA works but will require background knowledge in mathematics.

The last two methods of performing PCA are outside the scope of this book because they require more mathematics. The only method we'll consider here is the first method, which uses `prcomp()`.

We will use the integrated features in R to compute principal components and put them to work for us. Here is the simple framework we will follow:

- We will start with an unlabeled data set composed of a number of feature variables.

- Then we'll perform pre-processing on the data: mean normalization (each feature will have exactly 0 mean) and, optionally, feature scaling, depending on whether your data has different ranges of values (e.g., square feet of a house might range from 1500-5000, but the number of bedrooms might range from 1-4). Feature scaling will adjust the values to have a comparable range.

- We'll compute the first few principal components along with something called the *loadings vector,* which contains the information we'll use later. Using the loadings, we can compute the *scores* of the principal components. The positions of each observation in the new coordinate system of principal components are called scores and are calculated as linear combinations of the original variables and the weights in the loadings vector.

- Once we have computed the principal components, we'll plot them against each other in order to produce low-dimension views of the data.

- We produce a *biplot* graph that represents both the principal component scores and the loading vectors in a single display.

- Use the *scree plot* to depict the proportion of variance explained by each of the principal components to determine how many principal components are required to explain a sizable amount of the variation in the data; i.e., how low of a dimension can we get away with and still capture the essence of the data.

We'll see that using PCA involves much subjective effort in making decisions about how to use the principal components. In fact, there is no accepted objective method to decide how many principal components are enough and when more are required. Once you use PCA enough times, you'll get a feel for how best to use it.

Note that principal component analysis does not always reduce the dimension of the data. Indeed, if the original variables are already *uncorrelated,* then the analysis does nothing at all! The principal components, in this case, are the same as the original variables. The best results are obtained when the original variables are highly correlated because it is likely that most of the variables are measuring similar things, so there is a lot of redundancy in the original data. Categorical variables should not be included in the data set given to PCA; only continuous variables should be used.

A biplot is often used with a principal components analysis to assist in interpreting the analysis. A biplot displays the principal component scores and vectors representing the contribution of each of the original variables to these components on the same plane. In the context of principal component analysis, it plots the first two components and the original variables, the latter as direction vectors with the direction indicating the relationship between the principal components and the original variables. A principal component analysis makes as many components as there are variables. You choose the number of principal components you wish to use by determining the percentage of variance retained. Fortunately, the process orders the components by the amount of variance represented. We can begin demonstrating PCA by using an extended example with the USArrests data set, which is part of the base R package. Let's start by becoming familiar with the data set. This data set contains statistics in arrests per 100,000 residents for assault, murder, and rape in each of the 50 US states in 1973. Also given is the percent of the population living in urban areas.

```
> data(USArrests)          # 50x4 data frame
> names(USArrests)
[1] "Murder"  "Assault" "UrbanPop" "Rape"
```

As is the norm when using any new data set for analysis, you should use summary() to delivery some basis statistics:

```
> summary(USArrests)
     Murder          Assault          UrbanPop          Rape
 Min.   : 0.800   Min.   : 45.0   Min.   :32.00   Min.   : 7.30
 1st Qu.: 4.075   1st Qu.:109.0   1st Qu.:54.50   1st Qu.:15.07
 Median : 7.250   Median :159.0   Median :66.00   Median :20.10
 Mean   : 7.788   Mean   :170.8   Mean   :65.54   Mean   :21.23
 3rd Qu.:11.250   3rd Qu.:249.0   3rd Qu.:77.75   3rd Qu.:26.18
 Max.   :17.400   Max.   :337.0   Max.   :91.00   Max.   :46.00
```

We see that the mean is very different for each variable. For example, there are approximately eight times as many assaults as murders, on average. We can also check the variances of the variables using the apply() function. Notice that they are widely varied. This means we must scale the variables before performing PCA. This is always an important diagnostic task when using PCA so the data has mean zero and standard deviation one.

```
> apply(USArrests, 2, var)
   Murder     Assault   UrbanPop        Rape
 18.97047  6945.16571  209.51878    87.72916
```

Now we can perform PCA using the prcomp() function. The default behavior of this function is to center the variables to have mean zero, so the center=TRUE argument is not necessary. You should, however, specify the scale=TRUE argument so that the variables will have standard deviation one.

```
> pca <- prcomp(USArrests, scale=TRUE, center=TRUE)
```

The prcomp() function produces a number of useful outputs. The complete list can be obtained with:

```
> names(pca)
[1] "sdev"    "rotation" "center"  "scale"  "x"
```

The pca$center component displayed below contains the mean of the variables used for scaling. You should compare it with the values included above with `summary()` to see how they match up. The `pca$scale` component contains the standard deviation of the variables. If you square the standard deviation, by definition you will get the variance. These calculated values will match the values used with the `apply()` function above. The `pca$sdev` component contains the standard deviation of the principal components.

```
> pca$center
Murder  Assault UrbanPop     Rape
 7.788  170.760   65.540   21.232
> pca$scale
  Murder   Assault  UrbanPop      Rape
4.355510 83.337661 14.474763  9.366385
> pca$scale^2
  Murder    Assault   UrbanPop      Rape
18.97047 6945.16571  209.51878  87.72916
```

Next is the `pca$rotations` component, which is important to the use of PCA. The *rotations matrix* contains the principal component loadings, i.e., each column of `pca$rotations` is the corresponding principal component *loading vector*. In our example, we see four loading vectors: `PC1`, `PC2`, `PC3`, and `PC4`, which implies four principal components. In general, if the number of observations in your data set is larger than the number of variables, then the number of principal components will be equal to the number of variables. When you use the mathematical concept of matrix multiplication with `pca$rotations` and with the `USArrests` data set, you get the coordinates of the data in the rotated coordinate system. These coordinates are called the principal component *scores*. We'll see in a moment that matrix multiplication is not required since we can use the `pca$x` component instead.

```
> pca$rotation
                 PC1         PC2         PC3         PC4
Murder    -0.5358995   0.4181809  -0.3412327   0.64922780
Assault   -0.5831836   0.1879856  -0.2681484  -0.74340748
UrbanPop  -0.2781909  -0.8728062  -0.3780158   0.13387773
Rape      -0.5434321  -0.1673186   0.8177779   0.08902432
```

The `pca$x` component contains the value of the rotated data—the centered (and scaled, if requested) matrix multiplied by the rotation matrix `pca$rotation`. The dimension of `pca$x` is 50 by 4, the number of observations by the number of principal components. The `pca$x` component contains the dimensionality reduced data set you can use instead of the higher dimension data set you started with. We'll see how to select the data from `pca$x` shortly.

Now let's perform some exploratory data analysis with our `prcomp` object `pca`. We can use the `biplot()` function results in Figure 8-15. The biplot allows us to plot the principal components against each other to produce low-dimensional views of the data. The reason it is called a "biplot" is because it displays both the principal component scores and the principal component loadings in a single plot. The state names appearing in the plot represent the scores for the first two principal components. The arrows indicate the first two principal component loading vectors with the axes for each located on the top and right of the plot.

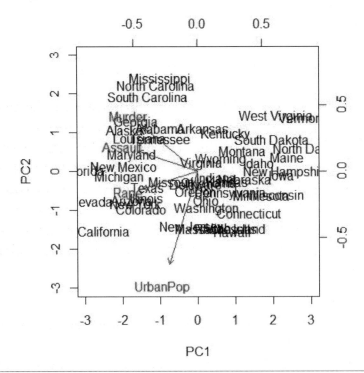

Figure 8-15 Plot of the first two principal components

For example, the word "Assault" is centered at the coordinate (-0.58, 0.19), where -0.58 is its loading on the first principal component and 0.19 is its loading on the second principal component. The arrows point in the direction of most variance; i.e., the direction in the feature space along which the data vary the most.

```
> biplot(pca, scale=0)
```

Now we can turn our attention to one of the most important aspects of PCA, selecting the principal components that explain the largest proportion of variance in the data. This will allow us to reduce the dimensionality of the data. We start by calculating the amount of variance explained by each principal component by squaring the pca$sdev component. Then we compute the proportion of variance explained by each principal component by dividing by the sum of the variances.

```
> pca_var=pca$sdev^2
> pca_var
[1] 2.4802416 0.9897652 0.3565632 0.1734301
> pve <- pca_var/sum(pca_var)
> pve
[1] 0.62006039 0.24744129 0.08914080 0.04335752
```

The results shown in pve are very telling. We see that the first principal component explains 62.0% of the variance in the data, while the second principal component explains 24.7% of the variance. This can be explained by a special plot called a *scree plot,* as shown in the left-hand part of Figure 8-16. The scree plot depicts the proportion of variance explained by each of the four principal components in the USArrests data set. The right-hand part of the figure shows the cumulative proportion of variance explained by the four principal components. With these plots, we can determine the dimensionality reduction. Here is the code for the plots:

```
> par(mfrow=c(1,2))
> plot(pve, xlab="Principal Component", ylab="Proportion of Variance
    Explained", ylim=c(0,1),type='b')
> plot(cumsum(pve), xlab="Principal Component", ylab="Cumulative
    Proportion of Variance Explained", ylim=c(0,1),type='b')
```

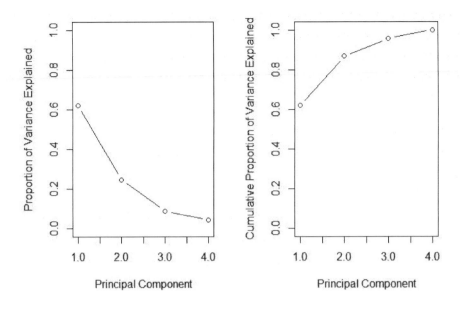

Figure 8-16 Scree plot showing proportion of variance and cumulative proportion explained

From the plots we can see that the first and second principal components explain a combined 86.7% of the variance in the data. By adding the third principal component, we get 95.6%, which is a very good representation of the entire data set. Now that we have a better understanding of the data and its principal components, let's explore how we can use PCA to our advantage.

Each new principal component can be interpreted as a new variable that is recorded for each observation. In the same way that each state has an `Assault` measurement, each state will have a PC1 value. In order to see the values of each observation on each principal component, we can use the `predict()` function. Here, d1 is a 50x4 matrix. Alternatively, we can do the calculation manually by matrix multiplying a scaled version of `USArrests` with the rotation matrix. These two methods are equivalent. The `predict()` function is a generic R function for predicting the results of various models. In this case, `predict()` recognizes pca as a `prcomp` object and calculates the value that each observation takes on each principal component.

```
> d1 <- predict(pca)
> d2 <- scale(USArrests, pca$center, pca$scale) %*% pca$rotation
```

Now we can use the first three principal components to calculate the new data set. Here, we've successfully reduced the four dimension data set to a three dimension data set. We can use a 3D plot to visualize the data, unlike before when it was not possible. We can use the `scatterplot3d` package to render the plot in Figure 8-16.

```
> d3 <- predict(pca)[,1:3]  # 50X3
> d4 <- scale(USArrests,pca$center, pca$scale) %*%
    pca$rotation[,1:3]
> library(scatterplot3d)
> scatterplot3d(d4[,1],d4[,2],d4[,3], main="3 Principal Components")
```

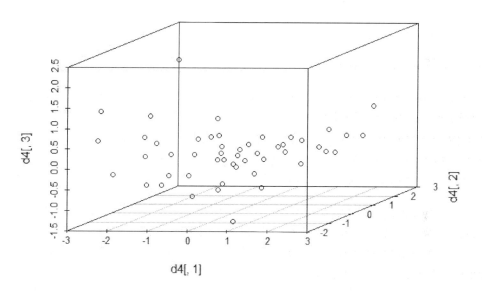

Figure 8-17 3D scatterplot using three principal components

Let's continue this dimensionality reduction process to yield a two-dimensional view of the data set using the first two principal components, which account for 86.7% of the variation. The 2D plot of the results is shown in Figure 8-18.

```
> d5 <- predict(pca)[,1:2]  # 50X2
> plot(d5[,1], d5[,2], col="blue", main="2 principal components")
```

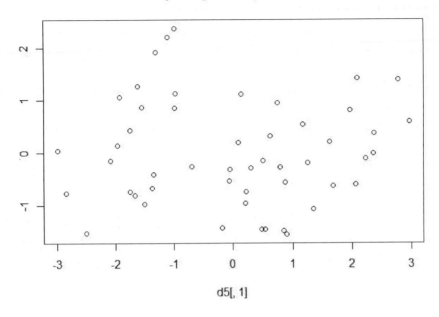

Figure 8-18 2D scatterplot using two principal components

In summary, PCA can be a useful tool for the following applications:

- When your supervised learning feature vectors have very high dimensionality (e.g., 10,000 features in a computer vision application), you can reduce the dimensionality of the data to speed up your machine learning algorithm for prediction. In this case, you'd use PCA on just the feature variables in your data set, setting aside the predicted variable. The result would be a lower dimension feature set that could be passed to a learning algorithm such as a neural net or logistic regression.

- By reducing the dimensionality of the data, you reduce memory/disk needed to store the data.

- You improve the visualization of the data by lowering the dimensionality in order to view in 2D or 3D.

SUMMARY

In this chapter, we've seen unsupervised machine learning through the use of a number of different methods including:

- Hierarchical clustering, an agglomerative (bottom-up) approach toward the clustering process.
- K-means clustering, a partitioning approach toward the clustering process.
- Principal component analysis, a sophisticated algorithm designed for dimensionality reduction.

Rather than the prediction and classification results we obtain through supervised learning methods, with unsupervised learning we get a more subjective sense of the data—namely, groupings of the data values.

Index

Bold page numbers contain term definition

Split data   146
    (train, test sets)

34455089R00158

Made in the USA
Middletown, DE
27 August 2016